21

R   cop. 4
622.007   Calif.   Division of mines
             Legal guide for California
         prospectors and miners.

Legal Guide

for

California Prospectors and Miners

Extensively Revised 1960 by
CHARLES L. GILMORE

Revised, 1962, by
RICHARD M. STEWART

STATE OF CALIFORNIA
EDMUND G. BROWN, Governor

THE RESOURCES AGENCY
WILLIAM E. WARNE, Administrator

DEPARTMENT OF CONSERVATION
DeWITT NELSON, Director

DIVISION OF MINES AND GEOLOGY
IAN CAMPBELL, Chief

Price $1

FERRY BUILDING, SAN FRANCISCO

FOREWORD TO THE THIRTEENTH EDITION

The number of editions through which a publication passes provides perhaps the one best index of its popularity. Judged by this standard, the *Legal Guide* is clearly the most popular item published by the California Division of Mines and Geology.

The first edition of the *Legal Guide*, brought out in 1931 under the title *Manner of Locating and Holding Mineral Claims in California*, was based upon the first *American Mining Law*, Bulletin 98, by the late A. H. Ricketts. Although Mr. Ricketts died in 1938, the next few editions up to and possibly including the fifth edition, published in 1939, undoubtedly had the direct benefit of this able mining attorney's extensive legal knowledge.

Further revisions and subsequent editions—bringing the number to eleven—were compiled by various members of the Division of Mines staff: C. McK Laizure, C. A. Logan, C. V. Averill, and L. A. Norman, Jr. The eleventh edition, compiled by L. A. Norman, Jr. in 1952, adopted the present name *Legal Guide for California Prospectors and Miners*. Reid J. Sampson, then Assistant Mining Engineer with the Division of Mines, was a major contributor to this compilation. The usefulness and demand for this edition was such that it was reprinted, with minor corrections, five times.

The twelfth edition was the result of a careful revision by the well-known Sacramento mining attorney, Charles L. Gilmore, who performed this solely as a public service.

This, the thirteenth edition, contains all of Mr. Gilmore's work. Some sections have been added to incorporate recent legislative changes, both state and federal, and all the sections have been reviewed and coordinated by Richard M. Stewart of the Division staff.

The general information contained herein is intended only as a guide and its application to specific legal problems should be referred to an attorney.

> IAN CAMPBELL
> State Geologist and Chief
> Division of Mines and Geology

March 3, 1962

FOREWORD TO FIRST EDITION

Among the questions most frequently asked of the staff of the State Division of Mines, both in oral interviews and in letters received, are those pertaining to points concerning the location of mining claims, the rights accruing thereunder, and the maintenance of those rights. These and other phases of the American Mining Law, both statutory and interpreted by judicial decisions, are dealt with in detail in Bulletin No. 98, of this Division, AMERICAN MINING LAW, by Mr. A. H. Ricketts, giving also a wealth of citations and related matter.

Although the bulletin referred to is written and presented in such language and arrangement as to be readily available and understandable to the layman, the engineer, and the lawyer, alike, we have found an insatiable demand for a simple and brief outline for distribution in an inexpensive pamphlet form. Such an outline covering the salient features needed by the average prospector and claim owner in initiating and maintaining his possessory rights to mineral ground, is the matter presented herein.

WALTER W. BRADLEY
State Mineralogist

San Francisco, November 27, 1931

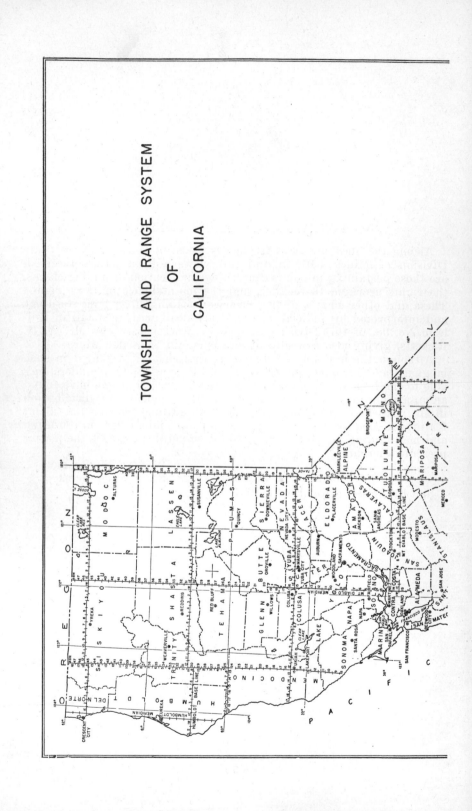

TOWNSHIP AND RANGE SYSTEM

OF

CALIFORNIA

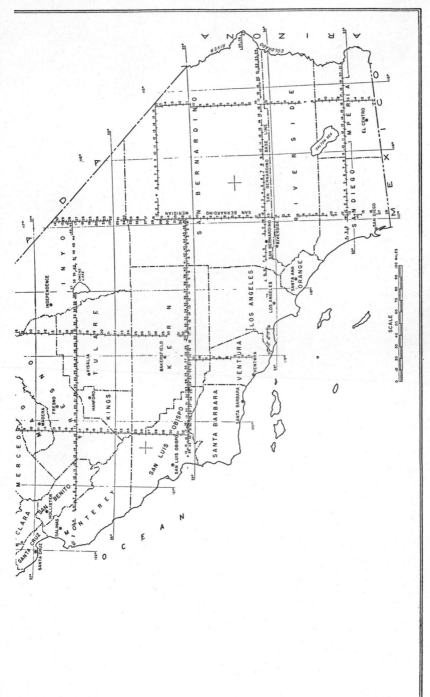

Township and range system of California.

CONTENTS

APPENDIX I

APPENDIX II

(9)

MANNER OF LOCATING AND HOLDING MINERAL CLAIMS IN CALIFORNIA *

By A. H. RICKETTS

Revisions by CHARLES L. GILMORE, Attorney at Law,
Sacramento, California

CONTENTS

* These notes are based upon *American Mining Law*, by A. H. Ricketts, State Division of Mines Bulletin 98, 1931 (republished as Bulletin 123, 1934), and briefly outline the salient information needed by the average prospector and claim owner in initiating and maintaining his possessory rights to mineral ground.

(11)

CONTENTS—Continued

Those laws and court decisions which have become effective since the last revision of 1952 have been added, and the later statutes should be carefully studied by prospectors and claim owners. They have, in many respects, changed entirely the old concept of mining locations and the conditions under which they may be made.

GOOD FAITH

Good faith, as an element in the initiation of mining rights under federal and state laws, is absolutely essential to the validity of such rights and may not be dispensed with; lack of it vitiates any attempt to initiate such rights.

LANDS

Lands Open to Location

(Sec. 2319, Revised Statutes of U. S.)

All valuable mineral deposits in public land of the United States, both surveyed and unsurveyed and the lands in which they are found, are free and open to exploration, occupation and purchase or lease, except that aliens may not obtain patent. Lands open to location include public mineral land within a national forest, unpatented parts of a congressional grant to a railroad company (except iron and coal), or an unconfirmed Mexican grant (to abide the final determination of the validity of the grant), also land within the limits of an unpatented townsite or when known to be mineral and under mining location at the time of the application for patent to the townsite, or an unlocated or unpatented "known lode" within the exterior limits of a patented or unpatented placer mining claim,* or mineral lands within an unpatented military or Indian reservation, or lands within power site reservations, or mineral lands restored to the public domain.

* But no one may go upon a valid existing placer claim to search for a vein without the claim owner's permission.

Land valuable for its mineral deposits is land which contains minerals in sufficient quantities and value to justify exploration and development. The mineral deposit may be metalliferous such as gold, silver, and other metals, or non-metalliferous such as alum, amber, building stone, coal, diamonds, gypsum and like substances; but under later congressional legislation popularly known as the Leasing Acts of 1917 and 1920, lands known to contain coal (see discussion, pp. 16-17), petroleum, oil shale, potash, phosphate and sodium salts cannot be located nor thereafter patented under the Lode or Placer laws, but are obtainable under lease, subject to the regulations and control of the Secretary of Interior. (Refer to page 46 for a comment on the regulations governing the mining of Leasing Act minerals.) The possessory right to a perfected location made prior to the passage of those acts however is not disturbed by their provisions.

Under the "Stock-Raising Homestead Act" (of December 29, 1916) there is a severance of the surface and mineral deposits and the latter may be located and worked in accordance with the mineral land law, with the right to enter and occupy so much of the surface thereof as may be required for all purposes reasonably incident to the mining or removal of the mineral; first, upon securing the written consent or waiver of the homestead entryman or patentee; second, upon the payment of damages to crops or other tangible improvements to the owner thereof, where agreement may be had as to the amount thereof, or, third, in lieu of either of the foregoing provisions he must execute a good and sufficient bond or undertaking to the United States for the use and benefit of entryman or owner of the land to secure the payment of damages to said crops and tangible improvements as may be determined by a court upon proceedings duly had and taken. All this seems to be giving a thing with one hand and taking it away with the other.

Determination of Lands Open

Several sources of information are available to aid in the determination of lands open to prospecting. Location of privately owned land can be obtained from the plat maps in the offices of the various county assessors. These plats, however, do not indicate those parts of the remaining areas that already have been the subject of unpatented mining claims. Surveys of unpatented mining claims are not required, and therefore, the exact location of these claims cannot be accurately plotted. The records pertaining to unpatented mining claims can be examined in the offices of the county recorders, and the records of patented mining claims in the offices of the U. S. Bureau of Land Management, Federal and Courthouse Building, Sacramento, or 1414 Eighth St., P.O. Box 723, Riverside, California.

In addition to examining all of these records, evidence for claims should be sought in the field. Location notices, discovery monuments, corner stakes, excavations, and local inquiry regarding recent work or occupation of the land are helpful.

When a determination has been made that the land in question is open public land, prospecting is permitted, and if a discovery of a locatable mineral is made, the land may be located as a mining claim.

Mining Locations on Mineral Leases

Under the Act approved August 13, 1954, and known as the "Multiple Mineral Development Law" (Public Law 585—83rd Congress *) the lands included in a permit or lease covered by an application or offer and known to be valuable for minerals subject to disposition under the Mineral Leasing Laws may be located for other minerals. Such location is made under the general Mining Laws and general mining shall be conducted so as to prevent damage to any Leasing Act minerals.

This Act is extremely complicated. It was originally designed to bring relief to those people who in the Colorado plateau area had made mining locations for uranium on lands they afterwards found out to be covered with uranium leases issued by the Atomic Energy Commission. To prevent bloodshed, action was necessary to enable mining locators and leasees, not only those with uranium leases but also those with oil and gas leases, to lie down in the same bed. This Act was the result. Of course it is a general law and under it, mining locations can be made on lands covered by oil and gas leases. However, as stated above, the Act was primarily for the benefit of uranium leasing and mining business in the Colorado plateau states.

Before any prospector goes abroad in any area where he has reason to believe there are leases outstanding, he had best study this Act and get competent legal advice as to its application to his particular problem before locating any claim.

Multiple Use Act (Public Law 167, 84th Congress, Approved July 23, 1955) †

This Act, hailed as a "Multiple Use Act," which was and is actually an amendment to the "Materials Act of 1947," provides that mining locations cannot be made on land containing sand, stone, gravel, pumice, pumicite, cinders and clay unless they have some peculiar valuable property not contained in the common varieties.
· Refer to Sec. 611 of the Act, reproduced in the Appendix to the guide, page 103, for a discussion of "common varieties." Paragraph 185.121 (b) of the Code of Federal Regulations, Title 43, Ch. 1, Part 185, further states:

" 'Common varieties' as defined by decision of the Department and of the courts include deposits which, although they may have value for use in trade, manufacture, the sciences, or in the mechanical or ornamental arts do not possess a distinct, special economic value for such use over and above the normal uses of the general run of such deposits. Section 611 of the law has no application where the mineral for which a location is made is carried in or borne by one of such common varieties."

However, what is a common variety is a question of fact determinable from the conditions peculiar to a particular deposit and its proximity to a commercial use site.**

Any mining location made subsequent to July 23, 1955 is made subject to the right of the United States to control or dispose of vegetative resources, including all timber thereon, and the right to con-

---

* See Appendix I, page 93.
** See paragraph A, Appendix II, page 115.
† See Appendix I, page 102.

struct access roads over and across the mining claim for use in connection with the production and control or sale of such vegetative resources.

On any location that was made prior to July 23, 1955, the United States has the right to publish a list of the areas whereon they claim the vegetative resources. Since the Act was passed the Bureau of Land Management has published and is now currently publishing a list of areas wherein probable mining locations exist that were made prior to July 23, 1955.

To protect his surface resources of such prior located claim, the owner must file his verified claim thereto. If he fails or neglects to file that verified claim within 150 days after the publication of notice, he loses the vegetative resources, and full control of the surface rights*; the Bureau of Land Management or the U.S. Forest Service, as the case may be, can harvest timber, build roads across his claim, and otherwise take control of the surface. They are not supposed to interfere with his mining operations. If by filing the verified claim within the allowable 150-day period he does not waive his surface rights, the owner will in all probability be forced to defend his rights in a hearing held by the Bureau of Land Management.

Should the timber on his claim be removed after loss of surface rights, and should he require timber subsequently and in the course of mining operations, the Government must supply him with timber for his mine use free of charge from the nearest appropriate source of supply.

Upon issuance of patent to the mining claim, the owner establishes full ownership of the surface and vegetative resources.

In order that any mining claim owner will be sure that he gets a copy of notice as published, he should if his claim was located prior to July 23, 1955, file a verified notice in the Land Office of the district wherein his claim is located, claiming the vegetative resources and demanding that any notice published under the Act be served upon him at the address he states in that notice. By this method he can be reasonably sure he is not going to lose his surface rights by default. This notice should contain the following:

1. Name and address of person making request;
2. the date of location;
3. the book and page of the recordation of the notice or certificate of location; and
4. the section or sections of the public land surveys which embrace such mining claim; or if such lands are unsurveyed, either the section or sections which would probably embrace such mining claim when the public land surveys are extended to such lands or a tie by courses and distances to an approved United States mineral monument.

Mining Claims Rights Restoration Act of 1955 (69 Stat. 681)

Under this Act of Congress (known as Public Law 359 † of 84th Congress) approved August 11, 1955, public mineral lands of the United States withdrawn or reserved for power development or power sites and not included in any project operating or being constructed

---

* See paragraph B, Appendix II, page 115.
† See Appendix I, page 107.

under a license or permit issued by the United States or an agency thereof, or under survey by a Federal licensee holding a preliminary permit, may be located the same as other public mineral land. No placer mining operations can be carried on for 60 days after the filing of a copy of the location notice in the Land Office. The Secretary of the Interior may within the 60-day period notify the locator there will be a hearing to determine whether mining will interfere with other uses and he will have the right after such hearing, to (1) prohibit placer mining altogether (2) permit mining if the operator will restore the surface to its original state or (3) grant general permission to engage in mining.

Any person holding an unpatented mining location on a Power Site located after the Power Site withdrawal was required to file a copy of his location notice in the Land Office within one year after the date of the approval of the Act. However, no penalty is provided for failure to file.

All mining on any claim located under the Act is at the risk of the miner and neither the United States nor a licensee under the Power Site Act will be liable for any loss or destruction suffered by the mining claim or any improvement or equipment thereon as a result of any Power Site development.

On locations made under the Act, the locator shall file a copy of his location notice within sixty days after the date of location and a copy of his affidavit of annual labor within sixty days after the expiration of each assessment year.

No facility or activity shall be erected or conducted on such location for any purpose other than mining. Summer homes or other non-mining structures are subject to immediate loss under this Act.

Section 624 of the Act contains the following sentence:

"Nothing in this Act contained shall be construed to limit or restrict the rights of the owner or owners of any valid mining claim located prior to the date of withdrawal or reservation."

Solicitor Bennett of the Department of the Interior, in 1958 ruled that all mining locations on land whether withdrawn before or after the Power Act withdrawal came under this law.

In *MacDonald* v. *Best* (N.D. 7858, July 14, 1960) Judge Halbert of the United States District Court for the Northern District of California, Northern Division, ruled the Department could not forfeit a mining location, made prior to power site withdrawal, for failure to file copy of location notice, as the exemption quoted above from Section 624 of the Act prevented forfeiture. Judge Halbert further ruled the Act contained no foreiture provision and suggested that the only method available to the Department to compel the filing would be by mandatory injunction.

Source Materials and Coal Deposits
Public Law 357—84th Congress

The Act, approved August 11, 1955 (69 Stat. 679), known as Public Law 357 of the 84th Congress, provides that lands that may be subject to the conditions and provisions of the Act of August 13, 1954 (Public Law 585—83rd Congress) and classified as or known to be valuable for coal, subject to disposition under the mineral leasing laws, unless embraced within a coal prospecting permit or lease, shall also be open to location and entry under the mining laws upon the discovery of a valuable source material occurring within any seam, bed, or deposit of lignite in such lands.

"Source materials" is defined as uranium, thorium or any other material which is determined by the Atomic Energy Commission, pursuant to the provisions of Section 61 of the Atomic Energy Act of 1954.

No extralateral rights shall attach to any mining location under this Act if made prior to May 25, 1955 and if based upon a discovery of valuable source material containing lignite. Mining locations under this Act shall be valid to the same extent as if such lands at the time of location and at all times thereafter have not been classified as or known to be valuable for coal, subject to disposition under the mineral leasing laws.

The locator or locators of such mining claim shall, not later than one hundred and eighty days from and after the date of the Act, post on the claim and file for record in the office where the notice or certificate of location is on record, an amended notice of mining location, stating that such amended notice was filed pursuant to the provisions of this Act and for the purpose of obtaining the benefits thereof. Copy of such amended notice must be filed within such period in the Land Office of the Bureau of Land Management for the state in which the mining location is situated.

By such location the locator acquires the right to mine on such classified lands valuable source materials in deposits other than deposits of leasing act minerals; the locator's rights shall include the right to mine, remove and dispose of lignite containing valuable source material and lignite necessary to be stripped or mined in the recovery of source material contained in the lignite.

On lands located on or after August 11, 1955 under this Act, the locator shall file a copy of his notice of location in the Land Office of the Bureau of Land Management for the state in which the claim is situated within 90 days after date of location.

There is a further proviso that the miner must report to the mining supervisor of the Geological Survey the amount of lignite mined or stripped in the recovery of the valuable source material during each calendar year and tender payment to him of ten cents per ton thereon.

All mineral patents issued under that Act shall be issued subject to the recording and payment requirements of the Act and shall contain a reservation to the United States of all leasing act minerals owned by the United States, other than lignite containing valuable source material and lignite necessary to be stripped or mined in the recovery of such material.

The holders of coal leases issued prior to the date of this Act or thereafter, if based upon a prospecting permit issued prior to that date, upon the discovery, during the term of such lease, of valuable source material in any lignite deposit within the leased lands will have the exclusive right to locate such source material under this Act. However, the mining and disposal of such source material shall be subject to the operating provisions of the lease and the provisions of the Atomic Energy Act of 1954.

An entryman or owner of any land or the assignee of rights therein [including rights to States wherein the coal deposits have been reserved to the United States, pursuant to the provisions of the Act of March 9, 1909 (35 Stat. 844) and the Act of June 22, 1910 (36 Stat. 583)] excepting lands embraced within a coal prospecting permit or lease upon the discovery of valuable source material in lignite within such lands, who, except for the reservation of coal to the United States, would have right to mine and remove the source material, is granted the same right to mine and remove lignite in connection with the mining of source material as any other locator under the provisions of this Act, subject to all other reporting provisions therein.

State Indemnity Selections of Mineral Lands

The Act of Congress approved August 27, 1958 (Public Law 85–771), amended Sections 2275 and 2276 of the Revised Statutes which provided for indemnity selections of nonmineral public lands by the state, in lieu of Sections 16 and 36 in each township lost to settlers, reserved for schools or colleges, adjudged mineral in character, found to be within Indian, military or other reservation, disposed of by the United States prior to survey, or lost through deficiencies in survey.

Under the original sections, the state could not select mineral lands, but under this statute the state may select mineral land in lieu of mineral lands lost to the state by appropriation prior to survey.

No lands on a known geologic structure of a producing oil or gas field may be selected except to the extent that the selection is being made as indemnity for lands on such a structure lost to the State or Territory because of appropriation prior to survey.

If selection is made of land subject to a mineral lease or permit, all land within that particular lease or permit must be selected and the state shall succeed to the position of the United States thereunder.

The lands to be selected under this statute must be unappropriated public lands of the United States, and which include, without otherwise affecting the meaning thereof, lands withdrawn for coal, phosphate, nitrate, potash, oil, gas, asphaltic minerals, oil shale, sodium and sulphur, but otherwise subject to appropriation, location, selection, entry or purchase under the Non-Mineral Laws of the United States, and including lands withdrawn by Executive Order 5327 of April 15, 1930, if otherwise available for selection.

The determination of mineral character of lands lost to the state and those made the base for indemnity selection, shall be made as of the date of application for selection and upon the basis of the best evidence available at that time.

The Bureau of Land Management has issued regulations governing these indemnity selections and anyone concerned or probably affected by this Act should obtain a copy of Circular 2024 of the Bureau of Land Management published in the Federal Register under date of September 18, 1959, and at the same time should obtain from the Division of State Lands, the policy the state intends to adopt and follow under this law.

This statement regarding this Act is printed herewith merely to show that under certain circumstances the state itself can acquire mineral lands.

Lands Not Open to Location

Land is not subject to mineral location when lying within a subsisting Indian, military, naval, national park, national monument (except Death Valley National Monument *), reservoir reservation, when withdrawn from sale by authority of Congress, or by an executive order express or implied; when situated below high tide; the bed of a navigable river; a lake bed if permanently covered with water (except Searles Lake in San Bernardino County); land within the limits of a congressional land grant to a state after approval of survey or certification by the land department; land which is occupied under color of title (unless it can be done peaceably); land which has passed into private ownership, patented land deeded to the state for unpaid taxes, land in national forests acquired under the Act of March 1, 1911 (Weeks Act); and land in a patented townsite after application for such patent has been made.

Prospecting Permits and Mineral Leases on State Lands

Mining locations cannot be made upon lands belonging to the State of California. Prospecting permits or leases are issued under rules and regulations of the State Lands Commission. Application should be made to the Commission for copy of their rules and regulations as well as copy of the appropriate application form governing the character of mineral deposit upon which a permit or lease is desired. Address your inquiry to:

STATE LANDS COMMISSION
Room 302, California State Building
217 West First Street
Los Angeles 12, California
Or
1108 O St.
Sacramento 14, California

Mining Claims Within National Forests

Generally speaking, vacant United States land within the boundaries of national forests is open to location and entry for mining purposes under the general mining laws, subject to the jurisdiction of the United States Forest Service. This subject is discussed on pages 67-68 and 116-117 of this guide.

Mining Claims Within Withdrawn Areas

A valid mining claim is not affected by withdrawal subsequent to its location, except that no annual expenditure is required during the period of such withdrawal.

DISCOVERY

In the world of mining law no word has been more defined than *discovery*. Each government bureau having jurisdiction and each court having the word before it has, from time to time, set about to tell us what it means. The net result has been obscurity rather than definition.

Neither hope nor expectation constitute a discovery. Under the "prudent man" concept, usually cited in defining the word, a discovery in a lode location means a vein or lode of rock in place bearing some valuable mineral sufficient in quantity and value to justify a person of ordinary business prudence to invest money therein in the effort to develop a paying mine. However, contemporaneous decisions seem to point to the apparent rule that the discovery must be of sufficient value

* See special regulations, Appendix I, pages 111-112.

to prove that the mine may be operated at a profit, however small.* A placer location must be supported by the same principles.

The discovery should be actual, but not necessarily of present commercial value; be situate within free territory and within the boundaries of the location, and may be upon or underneath the surface of the ground.

A lode location must be based on a discovery of rock in place bearing mineral, not necessarily in a fissure, nor with well-defined walls, but the location must include the top or apex of a vein or lode.

Only one discovery of a mineral deposit is required within a placer location, whether it be for 20 acres or an association placer of 160 acres.

A discovery can not be bisected by a side or end line to constitute discovery in two independent locations.

No location is complete until a valid discovery has been made.

LOCATIONS

Mining Locations

A lode location can legally cover only a vein or lode of quartz or other rock in place, enclosed by or suspended between walls of rock, but such walls need not be well defined. A placer deposit covers all other types of mineral deposits including building stone. There is no legal prohibition against the placing of both lode and placer locations on the same land by one locator, if conditions warrant. An example would be a partially eroded gold lode where the soil might carry free gold and the lode might be exposed by placer mining. Errors of any kind in a location which might render it void may be corrected by an amended location, in the absence of an intervening right. A "known lode" in a placer claim, if not specifically mentioned by the applicant for placer patent, and paid for separately, would become thereafter subject to lode locations by another if this can be done peaceably, but blind veins pass to the placer claimant without extralateral rights. In other words, in order for a placer claimant to obtain extralateral rights on a vein, blind or otherwise, within the boundaries of that claim, it is necessary that he file a lode location thereon and comply with the laws governing such claims. No person may enter and prospect for veins on a placer claim without consent of the claimant.

A mill site may be located on not over 5 acres of nonmineral land, not adjacent to a vein or lode, or it may be located upon lands which are prima facie mineral but which in fact are valueless as such. A mill site may be located in conjunction with a placer mining claim.

A tunnel-site claim may be located for the purpose of prospecting for blind veins not previously known to exist along the location line of the tunnel, for a maximum length of 3000 feet. The locator has the exclusive right to prospect for such blind veins along the tunnel's course and to locate 1500 feet in length upon any such vein that is cut or discovered in the tunnel.

In general, there are no hard and fast forms that must be used in locating claims and a location notice written in pencil will be as valid as any other, if the essential requirements are met. Examples of forms are

* See paragraph C, Appendix II, page 116.

shown herein for all four classes of claims mentioned above, and these may be safely followed. A valid mining location can be made upon a Sunday or holiday. Witnesses are not required, although of course there are occasions when it may be desirable to have them. [The latter part of this statement is especially true now that the California law allows 90 days in which to record a location. It should be noted that a location notice may be recorded at any time during the 90 day period.]

Locators

A location may be made without regard to the age, sex, or residence of the locator. One who has declared his intention to become a citizen may locate, but a location made by an alien, while not void, is voidable, and the locator may not obtain patent. It has been held that a convict on parole may locate. A corporation may locate to the same extent as an individual. There is no limit to the number of independent lode or placer locations which may be made by either a natural or artificial person, but each location must be based upon discovery therein. A dummy locator is one who joins in the location of an association placer mining claim in the interest of another person or of a corporation for the purpose of permitting such person or corporation to acquire more land than is allowed him or it by law. Such a location contemplates a fraud upon the government and is good only, say, as to 20 acres, but such a location can possibly only be attacked where the government is either actually or constructively a party as in an adverse suit.

Association locators not implicated in such fraud may select and hold their proportionate share of the location—that is, 20 acres each. An association placer mining location is not invalidated by an agreement made after the location and discovery of mineral, giving one person or a corporation an interest in excess of 20 acres.

The right to locate a mill site is limited to the proprietor of a noncontiguous vein or lode claim, or the owner of a quartz mill or reduction works, not owning a mine in connection therewith. By a recent act,* a mill site may be taken in connection with a placer claim.

Colocators are tenants in common; they are not mining partners unless they unite in working the claim.

Subsequent locators, having knowledge of the previous location, can not avail themselves of defects in the prior and subsisting location.

Essential Elements in Locating Mining Claim

The essential elements in locating either lode or placer claims are: discovery of mineral, marking the boundaries, posting the notice of location and the recording of an exact copy of same. The location notice *must* contain the following: (1) date; (2) name of locator or locators; (3) name of the claim; (4) the number of linear feet claimed in length along the course of the vein, each way from the point of discovery (in the case of a lode location) or the number of feet or acreage claimed (in the case of a placer claim); and (5) distance and direction as nearly as practicable from the discovery point to some permanent, well-known point, natural object or monument such as the confluence of streams, a bridge, hill or road intersection, except in the case of a placer claim

---

* See Appendix I, page 110.

located and described in the notice by legal subdivisions, where no other tie-in is needed. The location notice should be posted at the discovery point and it is customary to protect it from the elements in a box, tin can or cairn in plain view.

Boundaries

The location must be distinctly marked upon the ground so that its boundaries can be readily traced. These marks may be placed upon or off the claim or be put upon adjoining patented or unpatented ground but with no right to the ground within the overlap. The boundaries of unpatented claims may be shifted or the location floated, provided the rights of others are not affected thereby.

The federal law (see Sec. 28 Revised Statutes of U. S. cited hereafter) is silent as to the kind or position of boundary marks, but these details are supplied in part by the state statute (Chap. 4, Secs. 2302, 2303, Public Resources Code, cited hereafter). For lode claims, there shall be erected "at each corner of the claim and at the center of each end-line, or the nearest accessible points thereto, a post not less than 4 inches in diameter or a stone monument at least 18 inches high."

The state law is no more specific than the federal regarding the marking of the boundaries of a placer claim not located by legal subdivisions, beyond saying they shall be marked so that they may be readily traced. This law exempts the locator from the necessity of marking the boundaries of placer claims which have been located and described by legal subdivisions. Prudence will dictate care however, in taking advantage of this, as there is often great difficulty in actually finding and proving the identity of old section corners and quarter-section corners.*

Discovery Work

Within 90 days after the date of location of any lode or placer claim, the locator must sink a discovery shaft upon the claim to a depth of at least 10 feet from the lowest part of the rim of the shaft at the surface, or shall drive a tunnel, adit or open cut upon the claim to at least 10 feet below the surface.

The locator of a placer claim of 20 acres or less, may within 90 days after the date of location, excavate an open cut upon the claim removing not less than 7 cubic yards of material. If the placer claim contains more than 20 acres, the discovery work must consist of the performance of at least one dollar's worth of work for each acre included in the claim and shall be actual mining development work exclusive of cabins, buildings, or other surface structures, provided that this class of work herein named shall not be construed as a modification of the requirements as to depth of shaft, or the yardage of material required to be removed.

This discovery work in all cases must be made whether it is a new location or a relocation.

It has been decided by the courts that failure to do discovery work within the 90-day period after location does not forfeit the location if the work is done and an amended location showing the performances of discovery work is recorded prior to the time when some other person

---

* A map showing the Township and Range system of California is on pages 6-7; a diagram of section and township, may be found in Appendix I, p. 113.

should locate the same ground. Amended locations may be made at any time to cure any defective, erroneous or other matter required by law or if the requirements of the law have not been complied with before filing, provided such amendment does not interfere with the rights of others which have intervened.

Within 90 days after the posting of the Notice of Location on the ground, the locator shall record in the office of the Recorder of the county wherein the claim is situated, a copy of the same with a true statement of the markings of the boundaries and of the performance of the discovery work.

It is suggested as better practice and giving better notice to record the copy of the Location Notice immediately following the posting of the notice on the claim and thereafter proceeding with the marking of the boundaries and the performance of discovery work where such is required, and upon completion of that work fill in the statement of marking of boundaries and the performance of discovery work on the Location Notice that has been recorded, and then re-record the same document. By this method all possibility of a loss of proof of marking boundaries and performance of discovery work is eliminated.

Tying the Claim

It is essential that the posted notice and the record of the location contain a description of the claim located by reference to some natural object or permanent monument as will identify the claim. Speaking generally, any object or monument that will serve to identify the location will be sufficient, but the locator should select the most prominent object or monument possible under the circumstances. Stakes driven into the ground are the most certain means of identification of mining claims when there are no permanent monuments or natural object other than rocks or neighboring hills. The reference to such monuments or objects required by the mining law applies only when such reference can be made.

The reference made by the locator to the tie line is not, and is not intended to be, as accurate and correct as if made by a competent surveyor, but it should identify the location with reasonable certainty.

Lode Locations

Theoretically, a lode location should be in the form of a parrallelogram, having side lines 1500 feet along the course or strike of the vein or lode running 300 feet on each side of the middle of the vein or lode at the surface and with parallel end lines. But a lode location of less size and of different or any shape is valid; for instance, it may be in the form of a horseshoe or of an isosceles triangle; but such locations carry no extralateral rights. The side lines need not be equidistant from the middle of the vein at the surface and the end lines need not be straight nor of equal length; but its end lines must be parallel with each other or the location carries no extralateral right. If the side lines be across, instead of along the vein, they become the end lines and the location end lines become the side lines of the location as laid upon the ground; and the extralateral right is diminished accordingly. The presumption is that a lode extends to the entire length of the location, but nonmineral land within a placer location may be eliminated by the land department. A valid lode location includes the exclusive right of possession and enjoyment of the surface within its lines and of all veins or lodes having a top or apex within its lines. A location upon the dip of a vein or lode is invalid.

To make the location valid there must be compliance with the state laws as well as the federal laws in the manner of locating all mining claims, including lode claims. The federal mining law is merely a skeleton outline and the state law has filled in the spaces.

Within 60 days after the date of location of any lode mining claim the locator or locators must erect a post not less than four inches in diameter or a stone monument not less than 18 inches high at each corner of the claim and at the end centers thereof. This location must be carefully made so that the strike of the vein will follow down lengthwise of the location.

Placer Locations

The maximum size of a placer location is 20 acres for an individual and 160 acres for an association of not less than eight persons, or if the association is composed of less number, 20 acres for each individual therein.

A placer claim upon surveyed or unsurveyed public land must be located upon the ground in such shape and position as to conform as nearly as reasonably practicable to the lines of the public survey.

This means that if the location is laid upon unsurveyed lands such location, if reasonably practicable, should have east-and-west and north-and-south bounding lines, should be rectangular, if practicable, and in compact form.

The Notice of Location must be posted upon a tree, rock in place, stone, post or monument containing the name of the claim, the name of the locator or locators, date of location, number of feet or acreage claimed and such a description of the claim by reference to some natural object or permanent monument as will identify the claim located and by marking boundaries so that they may be readily traced.

When the placer deposit lies within a canyon, gulch, or an unnavigable stream, the placer location may exclude land not useful for mining purposes if conformity of location with subdivisional lines is unreasonable.

Tailings deposited upon public land initiate no right to dump thereon; but such land may be located as a placer mining claim by the producer or another or by the producer as a mill site, for dumping purposes, or it may be "scripped." If the tailings are allowed to flow upon the land of another, he is entitled to them. If the tailings are deposited so as to injure the land of another, without his consent, the latter may recover damages or injunctive relief may be granted.

The smallest legal subdivision recognized and provided for by the federal mining law is 10 acres, which must be square in form.

In order to prevent possible forfeiture of the claim under state law, a true copy of the notice of location should be recorded in the office of the local county recorder within 90 days of the date thereof.

Mill-Site Locations

The proprietor of a vein or lode claim or the owner of a quartz mill or reduction works may locate not more than 5 acres of nonmineral land not adjacent to a lode as a mill site in the same manner as the state law provides for the locating of placer claims. There is no certain form required for a mill site, but it may be noted here that 726 feet by 300 feet contains 5 acres. A mill site may be located in conjunction with a placer claim.*

A separate mill site is not, necessarily, complemental to each lode location. If the lode location is forfeited or abandoned, the right to the mill site is lost. There is no specific time within which a mill site shall commence to be used as such but the land must be used in good faith in connection with the ostensible purpose for which it was located. It may be located for pumping purposes. It may be located within a forest reserve but not within the limits of a railroad grant. Subsequent mineral discovery within the mill site does not affect the title thereto.

No annual expenditure is necessary on a mill site nor is any statutory expenditure required thereon when patent is applied for in conjunction with a lode claim, as the expenditure on such claim is sufficient.

Tunnel-Site Locations

In California the state law prescribes the manner of locating a tunnel site.

A discovery of mineral is not essential to create a tunnel right nor to maintain possession thereof. A failure to work the tunnel site for 6 months is considered an abandonment of the right to all undiscovered veins on the line of the tunnel. The line of the tunnel is the width thereof. The tunnel site must be located upon unappropriated public land and by diligently prosecuting work thereon its claimant has the right of possession of all veins or lodes within 3000 feet from its face on the line thereof, not previously known to exist, discovered in such tunnel, the same as if discovered from the surface. When the discovery is made the tunnel site owner is called upon to make a location on the surface of the ground containing the vein and thus create a mining claim.

All the owner of such tunnel has is the right of possession of all veins or lodes within 3000 feet from the face of the tunnel on the line thereof, not previously known to exist but discovered in such tunnel, to the same extent as if discovered from the surface. This right of possession is limited to 300 feet on each side of the vein thus to make up the standard width of a lode claim. The right to such vein dates by relation back to the time of the location of the tunnel. Surface mining claims located by another person subsequent to the commencement of the construction of the tunnel are taken and held subject to any rights of the tunnel owner thereafter developed. The tunnel site may be utilized for development purposes and the work may be credited as assessment work upon claims which are in fact benefited by it. A tunnel site can not be patented.

Townsites

No title can be acquired under a townsite entry to any vein of gold, silver, cinnabar, copper, or lead, nor to any valid mining claim or possession, held under existing laws.

---

* See Appendix I, page 110.

A valid mining claim, therefore, is not affected where it was known prior to the townsite patent that a mineral vein existed where the discovery was made; that is, land held as a valid and subsisting mining claim at the time of the issuance of the townsite patent, does not pass under such patent, nor is the title or right of possession of the location at all affected thereby.

Mineral land within a patented townsite can not be located.

There is no conflict between a lode or a placer patent and a townsite patent, and there can be none.

A mill site has been held to be a mining claim within the purview of the townsite act.

Amendment of Location or Record

The office of an amended location is to cure defects or supply omissions in the original location or in the posted notice or the record. The failure to perform discovery work within the required 90-day period may be cured by doing the work prior to an intervening right and filing an amended location notice to that effect.* An amended notice may serve to change the boundaries or the name of the claim or add the names of additional locators. It may include additional territory if without prejudice to the rights of others. It does not require additional discovery in the added ground, physical possession nor additional expenditure. It works no forfeiture of previously acquired rights not inconsistent with the amendment. It relates back to the date of the original notice where no adverse rights have intervened. It must be based upon a preexisting but not necessarily perfect location. It can not be made to exclude the name of a colocator without his knowledge and consent. It can not be made by a person who has parted with his title. There is no limit as to the time within which it may be posted or recorded.

Relocation

A subsequent location of a forfeited or abandoned mining claim is a relocation and not an original nor amended location. It is made in the same manner and is subject to the same conditions as an original location. It is void if it embraces a valid and subsisting claim. A valid relocation on the ground of forfeiture due to failure to perform annual labor cannot be made until after the expiration of the assessment year; i.e., after 12 o'clock noon on September 1; but if forfeiture is due to failure to observe state law, relocation may come after 90 days but an abandonment of the claim gives the right of immediate relocation. All improvements which are attached to or become a part of the realty pass to the relocator. The location rights, however, may be preserved by a resumption of labor in the absence of an intervening right. There can be no provisional relocations; that is to say, the validity of the relocation cannot be made to depend on whether or not the mine owner failed to do the annual work subsequently or may abandon his claim. A mining claim is not subject to relocation for failure to perform the assessment work if such work has been resumed after the expiration of the year and before any valid relocation is attempted. A person, holding confidential relations with the owner of a mining claim, for example, a lessee or optionee, who in violation of a contract or in breach of the trust

---
* See also page 33.

attempts to relocate the claim in his own name, will be held as a trustee for the rightful owner and he will secure no advantage by such act. A relocation by a cotenant inures to the benefit of his cotenants and he cannot by recording in his own name prejudice their rights nor forfeit his own undivided interest thereby. A relocator or other person may attack the verity of the recorded affidavit of labor and show its falsity. (See Sec. 2306, Public Resources Code of California.)

Conflicting Locations

The principle which governs the conflicting claims of appropriators of mining claims and other rights on the public domain is that, other things being equal, the prior locator prevails. A location made within the limits of ground already appropriated is void from the beginning; but the boundary marks of lode locations may be placed upon or across the surface of a prior location, or intervening ground whether patented or unpatented as mining or agricultural ground, for the purpose of securing an extralateral right; but no right is given to the ground within the overlap. If a locator should happen by mistake to place some of the monuments necessary to mark out his boundaries upon another's claim, the location is valid so far as that portion of the ground which was open to location.

Void Locations

Some instances of void locations are these: A location based upon a discovery which is within the boundaries of a prior claim; when located upon the dip of the vein or lode; a lode location of a placer deposit, or vice versa; a placer location intended to secure a known vein therein; to secure the timber growing thereon; a provisional location; a location or relocation based upon a breach of trust, or based upon trespass; a location without discovery where no attempt is made to discover the same; a discovery without boundaries; or, failure or neglect to comply with the local law in making the location on the ground.

Mining Claims on Stock-Raising Homesteads *

Patents to stock-raising or grazing homesteads reserve all minerals to the Government. Any qualified locator may go upon the lands entered or patented under the stock-raising homestead act to prospect for minerals, provided he does not damage the permanent improvements of the entryman; he also is liable for all damage he does to crops. (See Bureau of Land Management Circular No. 523, 43 CFR 168).

Notwithstanding the provisions of any Act of Congress to the contrary, any person who hereafter prospects for, mines, or removes by strip or open pit mining methods, any minerals from any land included in a stock raising or other homestead entry or patent, and who had been liable under such an existing Act only for damages caused thereby to the crops or improvements of the entryman or patentee, shall also be liable for any damage that may be caused to the value of the land for grazing by such prospecting for, mining, or removal of minerals. Nothing in this section shall be considered or construed to impair any vested right in existence on June 21, 1949. 30 U.S.C.A. 54.

---

* From U. S. Bureau of Mines Information Circular 7535, *Guide to Prospecting for Lode Gold and Locating Mining Claims on Public Domain*, February 1950, p. 18.

Anyone who has acquired the right from the United States to mine the minerals may re-enter and occupy as much of the surface as is required for mining purposes (1) by obtaining a written consent or waiver from the homesteader; (2) by payment for crops or tangible improvements to the owner under agreement; (3) by posting a bond of at least $1,000 to cover any damages that might be awarded by a court of competent jurisdiction. The bond must be filed with and approved by the manager of the Land Office. The Land Office will allow mineral applications on stock-raising homesteads, whether patented or held under entry, and patent will be issued in the regular manner except that it will contain the notation that the land is subject to occupancy and used in accordance with the act of December 29, 1916. [39 Stat. 862.]

FEDERAL STATUTES ON MINING LOCATIONS

The Revised Statutes of the United States governing mines and minerals have been codified and the principal Statutes are contained in Volume 30 of the United States Codes, cited and referred to by the Courts as 30 U.S.C.A., meaning Volume 30 of United States Code Annotated. The various sections of the Statutes have been transposed verbatime and re-numbered as Code Sections and will be so referred to in the following, all taken from 30 U.S.C.A. unless otherwise designated.

These laws are the basic provisions under which all rights to mineral deposits in "public lands" of the United States, such as California may be acquired. We here treat of minerals other than "source" or "leasing act" minerals.

Sec. 21.   In all cases land valuable for minerals shall be reserved from sale, except as otherwise expressly directed by law.

Sec. 22.   All valuable mineral deposits in lands belonging to the United States, both surveyed and unsurveyed, are hereby declared to be free and open to exploration and purchase, and the lands in which they are found to occupation and purchase, by citizens of the United States and those who have declared their intention to become such, under regulations prescribed by law, and according to the local customs or rules of miners in the several mining districts, so far as the same are applicable and not inconsistent with the laws of the United States.

Sec. 23.   Mining claims upon veins or lodes of quartz or other rock in place bearing gold, silver, cinnabar, lead, tin, copper, or other valuable deposits, heretofore located, shall be governed as to length along the vein or lode by the customs, regulations, and laws in force at the date of their location. A mining claim located after the tenth day of May, eighteen hundred and seventy-two, whether located by one or more persons, may equal, but shall not exceed, one thousand five hundred feet in length along the vein or lode; but no location of a mining claim shall be made until the discovery of the vein or lode within the limits of the claim located. No claim shall extend more than three hundred feet on each side of the middle of the vein at the surface, nor shall any claim be limited by any mining regulation to less than twenty-five feet on each side of the middle of the vein at the surface, except where adverse rights existing on the tenth day of May, eighteen hundred and seventy-two, render such limitation necessary. The end lines of each claim shall be parallel to each other.

Sec. 24. Proof of citizenship under Sections 21-24, 26-30, 33-48, 50-52, 71-76 of this title, may consist, in the case of an individual of his own affidavit thereof; in the case of an association of persons unincorporated, of the affidavit of their authorized agent, made on his own knowledge or upon information and belief; and in the case of a corporation organized under the laws of the United States, or of any state or territory thereof, by the filing of a certified copy of their charter or certificate of incorporation.

Sec. 25. Applicants for mineral patents, if residing beyond the limits of the district wherein the claim is situated, may make any oath or affidavit required for proof of citizenship before the clerk of any court of record or before any notary public of any State or Territory.

Sec. 26. The locators of all mining locations heretofore made or which shall hereafter be made, on any mineral vein, lode, or ledge, situated on the public domain, their heirs and assigns, where no adverse claims exist on the tenth day of May, eighteen hundred and seventy-two, so long as they comply with the laws of the United States, and with state, territorial and local regulations not in conflict with the laws of the United States governing their possessory title, shall have the exclusive right of possession and enjoyment of all the surface included within the lines of their locations, and of all veins, lodes, and ledges throughout their entire depth, the top or apex of which lies inside of such surface lines extended downward vertically, although such veins, lodes, or ledges may so far depart from a perpendicular in their course downward as to extend outside the vertical side lines of such surface locations. But their right of possession to such outside parts of such veins or ledges shall be confined to such portions thereof as lie between vertical planes drawn downward as above described, through the end lines of their locations, so continued in their own direction that such planes will intersect such exterior parts of such veins or ledges. And nothing in this section shall authorize the locator or possessor of a vein or lode which extends in its downward course beyond the vertical lines of his claim to enter upon the surface of a claim owned or possessed by another.

Sec. 27. Where a tunnel is run for the development of a vein or lode, or for the discovery of mines, the owners of such tunnel shall have the right of possession of all veins or lodes within three thousand feet from the face of such tunnel on the line thereof, not previously known to exist, discovered in such tunnel, to the same extent as if discovered from the surface; and locations on the line of such tunnel of veins or lodes not appearing on the surface, made by other parties after the commencement of the tunnel, and while the same is being prosecuted with reasonable diligence, shall be invalid, but failure to prosecute the work on the tunnel for six months shall be considered as an abandonment of the right to all undiscovered veins on the line of such tunnel.

Sec. 28. The miners of each mining district may make regulations not in conflict with the laws of the United States, or with the laws of the state or territory in which the district is situated, governing the location, manner of recording, amount of work necessary to hold possession of a mining claim, subject to the following requirements: The location must be distinctly marked on the ground so that its boundaries can be readily traced. All records of mining claims made after May 10, 1872, shall contain the name or names of the locators, the date of the location, and such a description of the claim or claims located by reference to some natural object or permanent monument as will identify the claim. On each claim located after the tenth day of May, eighteen hundred and seventy-two, and until a patent has been issued therefor, not less than one hundred dollars' worth of labor shall be performed or improvements made during each year.* On each claim located after the tenth day of May, eighteen hundred and seventy-two, and until a patent has been issued therefor, not less than $100 worth of labor shall be performed or improvements made each year. On all claims located prior to the 10th day of May 1872, $10 worth of labor shall be performed or improvements made each year, for each one hundred feet in length along the vein until a patent has been issued therefor; but where such claims are held in common, such expenditure may be made upon any one claim; and upon a failure to comply with these conditions the claim or mine upon which such failure occurred shall be open to relocation in the same manner as if no location of the same had ever been made, provided that the original locators, their heirs, assigns, or legal representatives, have not resumed work upon the claim after failure and before such location. Upon the failure of any one of several co-owners to contribute his proportion of the expenditures required hereby, the co-owners who have performed the labor or made the improvements may, at the expiration of the year, give such delinquent co-owner personal notice in writing or notice by publication in the newspaper published nearest the claim for at least once a week for ninety days, and if at the expiration of ninety days after such notice in writing or by publication such delinquent should fail or refuse to contribute his proportion of the expenditure required by this section his interest in the claim shall become the property of his co-owners who have made the required expenditures.

The period within which the work required to be done annually on all unpatented mineral claims located since May 10, 1872, including such claims in the State of Alaska, shall commence at 12 o'clock meridian on the 1st day of September succeeding the date of location of such claim.

Where a person or company has or may run a tunnel for the purposes of developing a lode or lodes, owned by said person or company, the money so expended in said tunnel shall be taken and considered as expended on said lode or lodes, whether located prior to or since May 10, 1872; and such person or company shall not be required to perform work on the surface of said lode or lodes in order to hold the same as required by this section. On all such valid claims the annual period ending December 31, 1921, shall continue to 12 o'clock meridian July 1, 1922.

CALIFORNIA STATUTES GOVERNING LOCATION OF MINING CLAIMS

The federal statutes outline in a general way the methods to be followed in locating claims, but the state statutes, which have grown out of the miners' customs and district rules which in many cases antedated the federal law, go into details about the requirements. The sections of the Public Resources Code of California quoted below give in full detail the requirements for making valid locations in this state.

* Geological, geochemical, or geophysical surveys may be considered as "labor." See Appendix I, page 109.

Public Resources Code, California *

Sec. 2301. Contents and Posting of Lode Location Notice

Any person, a citizen of the United States, or who has declared his intention to become a citizen, who discovers a vein or lode of quartz, or other rock in place, bearing gold, silver, cinnabar, lead, tin, copper, or other valuable deposit, may locate a claim upon such vein or lode, by defining the boundaries of the claim, in the manner hereinafter described, and by posting a notice of such location, at the point of discovery. The notice shall contain:

(a) The name of the lode or claim.

(b) The name of the locator or locators.

(c) The number of linear feet claimed in length along the course of the vein, each way from the point of discovery, with the width on each side of the center of the claim, and the general course of the vein or lode, as near as may be.

(d) The date of location.

(e) Such a description of the claim by reference to some natural object, or permanent monument, as will identify the claim located.

(The first paragraph is a rather loosely worded and incomplete repetition of Sections 22 and 23 of the Revised Statutes of the United States, quoted above. The balance specifically sets forth the five essential items needed to make a valid location notice, and should be carefully followed.)

Sec. 2302. Defining Boundaries, Marking Corners

The locator or locators of any lode mining claim shall define the boundaries of the claim so that they may be readily traced, but in no case shall the claim extend more than 1,500 feet along the course of the vein or lode, nor more than 300 feet on either side thereof as measured from the center line of the vein at the surface. Within 60 days after the date of location of any lode mining claim hereafter located, the locator or locators shall erect at each corner of the claim and at the center of each end line, or the nearest accessible points thereto, a post not less than four inches in diameter, or a stone monument at least 18 inches high.

Sec. 2303. Manner of Locating, Marking or Describing Placer Mining Claims

The location of a placer claim shall be made in the following manner:

(a) By posting thereon, upon a tree, rock in place, stone, post, or monument, a notice of location, containing the name of the claim, name of the locator or locators, date of location, number of feet or acreage claimed, and such a description of the claim by reference to some natural object or permanent monument as will identify the claim located.

(b) By marking the boundaries so that they may be readily traced.

Where the United States survey has been extended over the land embraced in the location, however, the claim may be taken by legal subdivisions and no other reference than those of such survey shall be re-

---

* Parts in italics and within parenthesis are revisors' comment, not part of law.

quired, and the boundaries of a claim so located and described need not be staked or monumented. The description by legal subdivisions shall be deemed the equivalent of marking.

(This section supplies details which are lacking in the federal statutes for this type of location. It does not, however, specify an exact way of marking a placer claim, as is done for quartz claims. When possible, placer claims should be located by legal subdivisions, as the land office will in practically every case require such conformity with public survey lines before issuing patent. Expense and delay will be saved by locating in this way.)

Sec. 2304. Discovery Work on Mining Claims

(a) Within 90 days after the date of location of any lode mining or placer claim hereafter located, the locator or locators thereof shall sink a discovery shaft upon the claim to a depth of at least 10 feet from the lowest part of the rim of the shaft at the surface, or shall drive a tunnel, adit, or open cut upon the claim to at least 10 feet below the surface.

(b) In lieu of the discovery work required by paragraph (a) of this section, the locator of a placer mining claim may, within 90 days of the date of location, excavate an open cut upon the claim, removing from the cut not less than seven cubic yards of material.

(This provision was intended to curb a heretofore prevalent abuse of the liberal federal statute which allowed holding a mining claim for a maximum period of nearly two years without doing any work. The original requirement as made effective in September 1935, called for enough work to expose the deposit upon which discovery and location was based. In the case of placer locations on buried ancient channels so common in California, it would usually be impossible for the average locator to do this within 90 days. The statute was accordingly amended to the present form in 1939.)

Sec. 2305. Discovery Work on Association Placer Claims

Within 90 days after the date of location of any placer mining claim hereafter located containing more than 20 acres, the locator or locators thereof shall perform at least one dollar's ($1) worth of work for each acre included in the claim. This work may all be done at one place on the claim if so desired, and shall be actual mining development work exclusive of cabins, buildings, or other surface structures. Nothing in this section shall be construed as a modification of the requirements of Section 2304 of this code.

Sec. 2306. Relocations—Discovery Work on Same

The relocation of any lode or placer mining location which is subject to relocation shall be made as an original location is required to be made, except that the relocator may either sink a new shaft upon the ground relocated to the depth of at least 10 feet from the lowest part of the rim of the shaft at the surface, or drive a new tunnel, adit, or open cut upon the ground to at least 10 feet below the surface; or the relocator may sink the original discovery shaft 10 feet deeper than it is at the time of relocation, or drive the original tunnel, adit, or open cut upon the claim 10 feet further or, in the case of placer mining claims, relocator may either excavate a new open cut upon the claim, removing from the cut not less than seven cubic yards of material, or remove from the original open cut not less than seven additional cubic yards of material.

Sec. 2306.5. Perfecting Certain Placer Claim Locations

(This provision allowed a period of 90 days, beginning September 19, 1939, to complete discovery work as required in the amended law Sec. 2304(b) on those placer claims where literal compliance with the previous requirement had not been feasible.)

Sec. 2307. Penalty for Non-Compliance with Code

The failure or neglect of the locator or locators to comply with the requirements of Sections 2301, 2302, 2304, 2305 or 2306 of this code shall render the location null and void (and no portion of the area within the location shall be subject to relocation by the same locator or locators within the period of three years from the date of the void location).

(The penalty imposed hereunder should not be confused with that resulting from the failure to perform annual assessment work, as covered in Sec. 2321. Under Sec. 2307, the failure to comply with any of the provisions of the state code may result in the claim becoming open to relocation by others in 90 days or less after the date of original location. See MacDonald v. Midland Min. Co., 139 C. A. 2d 304, which declares that though discovery work was not done within the 90-day period, if it is done thereafter and amended location notice is filed with the statement of discovery work before any other location is made, the error is cured and the location is good.)

Sec. 2308. Location of Tunnel Right

The locator of a tunnel right or location, shall locate his tunnel right or location by posting a notice of location at the face or point of commencement of the tunnel, which notice shall contain:

(a) The name of the locator or locators.

(b) The date of the location.

(c) The proposed course or direction of the tunnel.

(d) Such a description of the tunnel by reference to some natural object or permanent monument as will identify the claim or tunnel right.

(This section gives the modus operandi for exercising the right given in Section 27, Revised Statutes of the United States. Refer also to the suggested location form herein.)

Sec. 2309. Marking Boundary Lines of Tunnel Location

The boundary lines of the tunnel shall be established by stakes or monuments placed along the lines at an interval of not more than 600 feet from the face or point of commencement of the tunnel to the terminus of 3,000 feet therefrom.

Sec. 2310.   Amended Location Notice

If at any time the locator of any mining claim, or his assigns, appre-hends that his original location notice was defective, erroneous, or that the requirements of the law had not been complied with before filing, or in case the original notice was made prior to the passage of this chapter, and he is desirous of securing the benefit of this chapter, such locator, or his assigns, may file an amended notice, subject to the provisions of this chapter, if such amended location notice does not interfere with the existing rights of others at the time of posting and filing the amended location notice. No amended location notice or the record thereof shall preclude the claimant or claimants from proving any such title as he or they may have held under previous locations.

Sec. 2311.   Survey Notes and Certificate Part of Record

Where a locator, or his assigns, has the boundaries and corners of his claim established by a United States deputy mineral surveyor, or a licensed surveyor of this state, and his claim connected with the corner of the public or minor surveys of an established initial point, and incorporates into the record of the claim the field notes of such survey, and attaches to and files with such location notice a certificate of the surveyor setting forth (a) that the survey was actually made by him, giving the date thereof, (b) the name of the claim surveyed and the location thereof, and (c) that the description incorporated in the declaratory statement is sufficient to identify the claim, such survey and certificate becomes a part of the record, and such record is prima facie evidence of the facts therein contained.

Sec. 2312.   Mill Site Locations

The proprietor of a vein or lode claim or mine, or the owner of a quartz mill or reduction works, or any person qualified by the laws of the United States may locate not more than five acres of nonmineral land as a mill site. The location shall be made in the same manner as required for locating placer claims.*

(See also suggested form for location included herewith.)

(A mill site must be used in good faith for mining or milling purposes in connection with the operation of a lode or placer mine; but if for mining purposes, these must be auxiliary to, and not actually the extraction of, mineral.)

Sec. 2313.   Recording Copy of Location Notice

Within 90 days after the posting of his notice of location upon a lode mining claim, placer claim, tunnel right or location, or mill site claim or location, the locator shall record a true copy of the notice together with a statement of the markings of the boundaries as required in this chapter, and of the performance of the required discovery work, in the office of the county recorder of the county in which such claim is situ-ated. (Amended by Stats. 1957, Ch. 1089).

(There are now available printed location notice forms which include the form of notice showing performance of discovery work, and these are convenient. If not available, the forms given herein may be copied and attached to the location notice before having it recorded.)

---

* A mill site also may be located in connection with a placer claim. See Appendix I, page 110.

Sec. 2314. Annual Work Required

The amount of work done or improvements made during each year to hold possession of a mining claim shall be that prescribed by the laws of the United States, to wit: One hundred dollars ($100) annually.

Sec. 2315. Affidavit of Annual Labor

Whenever a mine owner has performed the labor and made the improvements required by law upon any mining claim, the person in whose behalf such labor was performed or improvements made, or some one in his behalf shall, within 30 days after the time limited for performing such labor or making such improvements, make and have recorded by the county recorder, in books kept for that purpose, in the county in which the mining claim is situated, an affidavit setting forth the value of labor or improvements, the name of the claim, and the name of the owner or claimant of the claim at whose expense the labor was performed or the improvements were made. The affidavit, or a copy thereof, duly certified by the county recorder, shall be *prima facie* evidence of the performance of such labor or the making of such improvements, or both.

(When work is required, the time for filing the above affidavit expires at the end of 30 days after noon of September 1.)

Sec. 2321. Effect of Failure to Perform Required Work: Suspension of Right of Relocation

The failure or neglect of any locator of a mining claim to perform development work of the character, in the manner, and within the time required by the laws of the United States shall disqualify such locator from relocating the ground embraced in the original location or mining claim or any part thereof under the mining laws, within three years after the date of his original location, and any attempted relocation thereof by any of the original locators shall render such location void. (Enacted 1939.)*

Sec. 2322. Admissibility in Evidence of Location Records: Force and Effect

The record of any location of a mining claim, mill site, or tunnel right in the office of the county recorder, as provided in this chapter, shall be received in evidence and have the same force and effect in the courts of the State as the original notice. (Enacted 1939.)

Sec. 2323. Rules Governing Admission of Copies of Records

Copies of the records of all instruments required to be recorded by this chapter, duly certified by the recorder in whose custody such records are, may be read in evidence under the same circumstances and rules as are provided by law for using copies of instruments relating to real estate, duly executed or acknowledged or proved and recorded. (Enacted 1939.)

Sec. 2324. Construction of Chapter Provisions

The provisions of this chapter shall not in any manner be construed as affecting or abolishing any mining district or the rules and regulations thereof within the State. (Enacted 1939.)

---

* See *Judson* v. *Herrington,* 71 C.A. 2d 565, 162 p. 2d 931, which declares the 3-year prohibition to be in conflict with the federal law. Reprinted in California Div. Mines Rept. 42, pp. 57-60, 1946.

ANNUAL EXPENDITURE OR ASSESSMENT WORK

Annual expenditure consists of labor * done or improvements made upon both lode and placer claims and must be *worth* at least one hundred dollars. It must be done or made before 12 o'clock noon of the first day of September of each year subsequent to the location year until patent or the receiver's final receipt has issued to the mine claimant (unless congress has declared a moratorium for that particular year, which must be consulted as each moratorium may, and usually does, vary in detail or unless the location was made prior to governmental withdrawal or the Leasing Act. Within withdrawn areas neither assessment work nor patent is necessary to preserve the possessory right of the claimant; and he holds his claim in perpetuity unless he loses his rights by abandonment). If not so made, and there is no resumption of labor the claim is subject to adverse relocation.

Assessment work may be done either underground or upon the surface, upon or off the claim itself, if of benefit or value to it. Any work done for the purpose of discovering minerals is "improvements" within the spirit of the statute. Any building, machinery, roadway, or other improvement used in connection with, and essential to the practical development of the claim will enter into and form a part of the expenditure for improvements. Under some circumstances the services of a watchman may be counted as annual expenditure. In determining the amount of work done on a claim for the purpose of representation, the test is as to the reasonable value of said work, not what was paid for it nor what the contract price was, but it depends entirely upon whether or not said work was *worth* the sum of one hundred dollars.

Labor may be done or improvements made upon or at a distance from any one of the locations comprising a group of claims when of benefit and value to the entire group. Any location within the group not so benefited may become subject to forfeiture. The expenditure must equal in the aggregate the amount required on all the locations. The test of sufficiency is whether the expenditure tends to facilitate the development or actually promotes or directly tends to promote the extraction of mineral from or improve the property or be necessary for its care or the protection of the mining works thereon or pertaining thereto.

The amount of the annual expenditure upon a placer claim is the same whether for 20 acres or on an association claim of 160 acres; viz., one hundred dollars.

A certain number of days work at a certain sum a day, or work of a certain character or extent do not constitute the requisite expenditure under the mining laws.

Labor done or improvements made may be sufficient to hold the claim although not in fact paid for or when gratuitously performed; but payment for work not done will not suffice.

The annual expenditure may be made by the locator, his heirs, assigns or legal representatives, or by some one in privity therewith, or by one who has an equitable or beneficial interest. A stockholder in a corporation claiming the property, or a receiver appointed by a court are within the rule; but labor done or improvements made by a trespasser or stranger to the title will not inure to the benefit of the claimant.

---

* Geological, geochemical, or geophysical surveys may be considered as "labor." See Appendix I, page 109.

Annual expenditure is not required upon a mill site nor upon a tunnel site; but failure to prosecute the work on the tunnel for 6 months shall be considered as an abandonment of the right to all undiscovered veins on the line of such tunnel. Yet the work on it may count as annual labor on claims which it is so run as to cut and develop; or be applied as patent expenditure.

Wrongful adverse possession of a mining claim (by force) excuses the rightful owner or locator from doing the assessment work required by law, during the time of such adverse possession.

Annual assessment work may be applied to patent expenditure.

Location Work and Assessment Work Distinguished

Confusion of thought has arisen among mining locators as to the effect of the provision of the state mining law relating to location or discovery work upon both lode and placer mining claims as affecting the federal requirement of annual assessment work upon such locations. There is no conflict between the two laws nor is the one merged with the other. Hence, a location of either lode or placer may be lost * unless such location work is duly performed; and the possessory right to an unpatented location can not be maintained without due performance of the annual assessment work.

In other words, the state statute places an additional burden upon the mining locator, on claims filed on and after September 15, 1935.

Proof of Annual Labor

California mining law provides for the making, recording and legal effect of affidavits of annual expenditure. Within 30 days after the time limited for performing labor or making improvements upon a mining claim—that is, 12 o'clock noon of September 1—the mine owner or some one in his behalf may make and have recorded by the local county recorder an affidavit setting forth the value of the labor and improvements made, the name of the claim or claims, and the name of the owner or claimant of such claim at whose expense the same was made or performed. If this affidavit is filed before or within the said time, it presents prima facie evidence of the facts properly therein stated; but not otherwise. If filed after said 30 days, it has no legal effect. This affidavit does not prevent other proof by the claimant nor attack by his adversary. Neither the failure to record the affidavit nor a mistake therein will work a forfeiture of the location. Its due filing tends to prevent an adverse relocation.

Suspension of Annual Expenditure

At various times since 1893, Congress has suspended the making of annual expenditure during a stated period. The obsolescence of these enactments previous to the year 1931 deprives them of present interest.

By act of June 6, 1932, annual assessment work was suspended for the fiscal year July 1, 1931 to July 1, 1932. No filing of notice was required.

---

* See *MacDonald* v. *Midland Min. Co.*, 139 C.A. 2d 304, which holds that if amended location notice showing performance of location (discovery) work is recorded after the ninety day period and before any other location intervenes, the original location is good.

A similar act was passed in 1933, with the proviso that only those claimants entitled to exemption from the payment of federal income tax for the taxable year 1932 are benefited by this act and such claimants must file on or before noon July 1, 1933, notice of intention to hold their claims under this act. Assessment work was suspended for the year July 1, 1933 to July 1, 1934. This act also applies only to those claimants who were exempt from payment of federal income tax for the taxable year of 1933, who file their notice of desire to hold their claims under this act, as provided in the preceding act. This act further provided that no individual could claim exemption on more than six lode claims nor on more than six placer claims not to exceed 120 acres (in all), and that a partnership, association, or corporation is not entitled to such exemptions on more than 12 lode claims nor on more than 12 placer claims not to exceed 240 acres (in all). A substantially similar act was passed by Congress for the assessment years 1934-1935; 1935-1936; 1936-1937, and 1937-1938. No act for the suspension of assessment work for the year 1938-1939 was passed, but the time was extended from July 1, 1939 to September 1, 1939, in which to *commence* work, provided such work be "prosecuted with reasonable diligence to completion."

The acts of 1934, 1935, and 1936 omitted Alaska from their operation.

There was no suspension of assessment work for the years 1939-1940 or 1940-1941, except as provided in the Soldiers and Sailors Civil Relief Act, which was enacted in 1940. Under section 505 of this act anyone entering active service of the armed forces of the United States could file an intention to hold his claims until six months after termination of such service (or hospitalization), if the notice is filed by the expiration of the assessment year in which he entered the service.

Sec. 506 of the same law permits the suspension of mining operations on United States land held under permit or lease for a similar period and waives peyment of rentals or royalties for such period, provided that the permittee or lessee shall within 6 months after the effective date of the act, or 6 months after his entrance into military service notify the General Land Office by registered mail of his entrance into such service and of his desire to avail himself of this section. The above law was approved in time to affect work for the year ended July 1, 1941.

Congress passed an act, approved May 7, 1942, suspending assessment work on mining claims in the United States including Alaska, during the years July 1, 1941 to July 1, 1943, providing "notice of desire to hold" be filed on or before noon July 1, 1942 and July 1, 1943, also that such suspension "shall not apply to more than six lode mining claims held by the same person, nor to more than twelve lode mining claims held by the same partnership, association or corporation." No restriction was placed on the number of placer claims, nor on persons liable for payment of federal income tax. An act, approved May 3, 1943, waives assessment work for the duration of the then current war in the following language: "the same is hereby suspended as to *all* mining claims in the United States, including the Territory of Alaska, until the hour of 12 o'clock meridian on the first day of July after the cessation of hostilities in the present war as determined by proclamation of the President or concurrent resolution of the Congress: Provided, that every claimant of any such mining claim, in order to obtain the benefits of this act, shall file or cause to be filed, in the office where the location notice or certificate is recorded, on or before 12 o'clock meridian of July 1 for each year that this act remains in effect, a notice of his desire to hold said mining claim under this act.'' The President proclaimed the cessation of hostilities on December 31, 1946.

An act, approved June 17, 1948, suspends assessment work on all mining claims for the year July 1, 1947 to July 1, 1948: the filing, by noon of July 1, 1948, of a notice of intention to hold the claims being the only requirement.

H. R. 1754, which became Public Law 107, Eighty-first Congress, upon being signed by the President on June 17, 1949, provided: ''That the provision of section 2324 of the Revised Statutes of the United States, which requires on each mining claim located, and until a patent has been issued therefor, not less than $100 worth of labor to be performed or improvements aggregating such amount to be made each year, be, and the same is hereby, suspended as to all mining claims in the United States until the hour of 12 o'clock meridian of the 1st day of July 1949: Provided, That every claimant of any such mining claim in order to obtain the benefits of this Act shall file, or cause to be filed, in the office where the location notice or certificate is recorded, on or before 12 o'clock meridian of August 1, 1949, a notice of his desire to hold said mining claim under this Act: Provided further, That any labor performed or improvements made on any such mining claim during the year ending July 1, 1949, may be credited against the labor or improvements required to be performed or made for the year ending at 12 o'clock meridian on the 1st day of July 1950.

''Sec. 2. Notwithstanding the provisions of any Act of Congress to the contrary, any person who hereafter prospects for, mines, or removes, by strip or open pit mining methods, any minerals from any land included in a stock raising or other homestead entry or patent, and who had been liable under such an existing Act only for damages caused thereby to the crops or improvements of the entryman or patentee, shall also be liable for any damage that may be caused to the value of the land for grazing by such prospecting for, mining, or removal of minerals. Nothing in this section shall be construed to impair any vested right in existence on the effective date of this section.''

An act, approved June 29, 1950 extended the time for doing assessment work for the year 1949-1950, in the following words: ''That the time during which labor may be performed or improvements made under the provisions of section 2324 of the Revised Statutes of the United States, on any unpatented mining claim in the United States, including Alaska, for the period commencing July 1, 1949, is hereby extended until the hour of 12 o'clock meridian on the first day of October 1950; Provided, that assessment work or improvements required for the year ending at 12 o'clock meridian July 1, 1951, may be commenced immediately following 12 o'clock meridian July 1, 1950.'' It was further enacted June 14, 1950 (H. R. 6406) that any claimant wishing to obtain the benefits conferred by the second proviso of the first section of Public Law 107, 81st Congress, approved June 17, 1949, may file or cause to be filed by noon of July 1, 1950, a statement of the work done or improvements made during the year ending July 1, 1949, or such statement may be included as a part of the annual notice of the performance of assessment work for the year ending noon July 1, 1950. There was no suspension of assesment work for the year 1950-1951.

By the Act of Congress approved August 23, 1958, the period commencing in 1958 for the performance of annual assessment work commenced at 12 o'clock meridian on the first day of July, 1958 and ended at 12 o'clock meridian, September 1, 1959. Thereafter the annual assessment year commenced at 12 o'clock meridian September 1 and ended at 12 o'clock meridian September 1 of the following year.

Summary of suspensions of annual assessment work *
1932-1951

For assessment year ending noon July 1	Remarks
1932	Unconditional suspension of assessment work. (47 Stats. 290) (53 L.D. 703).
1933	Federal income taxpayers not exempt. Notice of intention to hold had to be filed. (48 Stats. 72) (48 Stats. 777).
1934 1935 1936 1937 1938	Same restrictions as above but with exemption limited to six lode claims or 120 acres of placer ground held by an individual, or 12 lode claims or 240 acres of placer ground held by a corporation. Acts of 1935, 1936, 1937 omitted Alaska. (49 Stats., p. 337) (49 Stats., p. 1238) (50 Stats., p. 306).
1939	Time for commencing annual work extended to Sept. 1 (Omitted Alaska) (53 Stats., pt. 2, p. 991).
1940	Assessment work had to be performed.
1941	Exemption for claim owners in the armed services of the United States until six months after termination of such service, or during any period of hospitalization or disability incurred in line of duty. Notice of intention had to be filed during assessment year in which claimant entered the service. (Public Law No. 861, Sec. 505) (76th Congress). The exemption noted above is in full force and effect.
1942 1943	Exemption limited to six lode claims for an individual and 12 lode claims for a corporation. All placer claims exempt. Notice of desire to hold had to be filed. (Pub. Law 542) (77th Cong., Chap. 294, 2d Session) (Pub. Law 47, 78th Cong.)
1944 1945 1946 1947	Notice of desire to hold had to be filed. (Pub. Law 47, 78th Cong.)
1948	As a result of the proclamation by the President on December 31, 1946, that hostilities had ceased, wartime suspension of annual assessment work ended July 1, 1947, but Public Law 665, 80th Cong., approved by the President June 17, 1948, suspended assessment work for the assessment year ending July 1, 1948.
1949	Notice of desire to hold had to be filed on or before August 1, 1949. Work performed during year could be credited against next year. (Pub. Law 107, 81st Cong.) Credit for such work could be obtained by filing a statement on or before July 1, 1950. (Pub. Law 544, 81st Cong.)

---

* From a similar summary in *Mining laws of the State of Oregon,* Oregon Department of Geology and Mineral Resources, Bulletin no. 1, 3d revision, p. 35, 1951, with additions and revisions.

For assessment year ending noon July 1	1932-1951—Continued Remarks
1950	Extension of three months (to October 1, 1950) granted to complete assessment work. Annual labor for year ending July 1, 1951 could begin immediately following July 1, 1950. (Pub. Law 582, 81st Cong.)
1951 to 1958 inc.	Assessment work had to be performed. No time extension authorized by Congress.
1958-59	Assessment work for the year beginning July 1, 1958 ended on September 1, 1959.
1959 and following	Assessment year September 1 to September 1

Deferment of Annual Labor

Under the Act of June 21, 1949 (30 U.S.C.A. 28 a-e), annual labor may be deferred for an initial period of one year and conditionally for an additional year where right-of-way over surrounding lands is denied or is in litigation, or other legal impediments affect right of entry to claims, upon the satisfactory showing by petition to District Land Office. All deferred assessment work shall be performed not later than the end of the assessment year next subsequent to the removal or cessation of the causes for deferment or the expiration of any deferments granted under Section 28b-28e of this title and shall be in addition to the annual assessment work required by law in such year. Claimant must record in the county where the claim is situated a notice to the public of the petition and also of the order or decision disposing of such petition.

Contribution

Persons who acquire undivided interests in a mining claim by location or otherwise are known as cotenants or co-owners, and any one or more who fail to contribute the proportionate share of the assessment expenditure may be "advertised out" by the remaining party or parties. This may be done by personal service, in writing, or by publication in a newspaper published nearest the claim for at least once a week for 90 days and if at the expiration of 90 days after such notice in writing or 180 days from the first day of such publication such delinquent or delinquents should fail or refuse to contribute his proportion of the expenditure required by law, his interest in the claim shall become the property of his co-owners who have made the required expenditures and given said notice. California law provides for the giving of such notice for contribution and the manner of establishing the same of record in the office of the local county recorder, and also of the fact of payment or nonpayment, as the case may be.

Resumption of Labor

A mine claimant who has failed to do the annual labor during the statutory assessment year may resume work at any time thereafter, in the absence of an intervening right.

To "resume work" is to begin work in good faith and diligently prosecute the same to completion before a valid adverse relocation, and thereafter the rights of the mine claimant are precisely what they were before the default.

Work is not resumed by the mere purchase of material or the mere bringing of the same upon the claim.

The Federal Leasing Act of 1920 did not have the effect of extinguishing the right of the locator under the mining act to save his claim under the original location by resuming work at any time after failure to perform the annual assessment labor in the absence of adverse relocation or intervening right.

PATENTS

A patent is not essential to the enjoyment of a mining claim. There is no restriction as to the time when it shall be applied for nor as to its use or sale. It confers no greater mining rights than those obtained by a valid location. It, however, establishes the exterior boundaries of the claim, that discovery has been made, and dispenses with the performance of annual labor. A patent is not always conclusive of the title, as, for one thing, it may, possibly, be shown that the patentee is an undisclosed trustee.

Lode, and placer locations upon unsurveyed lands, must be officially surveyed for patent. No survey is required for placer locations laid in conformity with legal subdivisions.

Detailed information relative to the procedure for obtaining patent to a mining claim will be found on pages 55-65 of this report.

Adverse Claims

When a patent is applied for, the owner of a prior conflicting location must duly institute adverse proceedings; otherwise, he will be treated in law as having voluntarily waived his prior and superior rights, and his adversary will secure a patent covering his location or a part thereof. The adverse must be filed in the local land office within the 60-day publication of the application for patent and followed by suit in a court of competent jurisdiction within 30 days thereafter and be diligently prosecuted to final judgment. No equitable title nor existing lien is disturbed by the issuance of the patent.

Protests

A protest may be filed at any time by any person before patent actually issues. The protest may be directed against the patenting of the claim as applied for upon any ground tending to show that the applicant has failed to comply in any matter essential to a valid entry under the patent proceedings; as for instance, that no mineral has been disclosed within the claim applied for, that the necessary expenditure of five hundred dollars has not been made by the proper party; or it may be filed by a cotenant excluded from the application for patent. A protest never can take the place of an adverse.

Right-of-Way Reservations

Reservation in patents of right of way for ditches or canals. 43 U.S.C.A. 945.

In all patents for lands taken up after August 30, 1890, under any of the land laws of the United States or on entries or claims validated by the Act of August 30, 1890, west of the one hundredth meridian, it shall be expressed that there is reserved from the lands in said patent described a right of way thereon for ditches or canals constructed by the authority of the United States. (Aug. 30, 1890, c. 837, Sec. 1, 26 Stat. 391.)

MISCELLANEOUS INFORMATION

Deeds

A mining claim can be transferred only by operation of law or by a deed in writing; but a discoverer of mineral may transfer his right of location by parol. A mining claim which has a known descriptive name may be sufficiently described by such name, coupled with a proper reference to the record, or if patented, to the survey number. That a claim is known by several names and only one of them is given in the deed is immaterial. Minerals may be granted without the surface, or vice versa. Where there is a severance, the owner of the mineral has a right to occupy so much of the surface as is reasonably necessary for mining purposes. No attesting witnesses to the execution of a deed are required. If the title to an unpatented claim stands alone in the name of one spouse, it is not essential to the title that the other spouse should join in the execution of the deed.

A quitclaim deed is sufficient to pass the title, if clear.

Fixtures

(Chap. 7, Sec. 2601, Public Resources Code of California.)

A fixture is an article which may or may not actually be affixed to the mine. In this state sluice boxes, flumes, hose, pipes, railway tracks, blacksmith shops, mills, and all other machinery or tools used in working, or developing a mine are deemed to be affixed to the mine. See also *Relocation,* page 26; fixtures pass to the relocator.

Forfeiture of Interest for Failure to Pay Share of Taxes

Chapter 1292, Statutes of 1945, effective September 15, 1945, provides that upon the failure of any co-owner of a mine or claim to contribute his proportionate share of the taxes which have been levied and assessed upon the mine or claim for the period of five years, the co-owner or co-owners who have paid such share may at the expiration of the five years serve upon the delinquent co-owner notice thereof. If the delinquent co-owner fails or refuses to contribute his share of such taxes within 90 days after the service of such notice, the co-owner contributing such share may file in the superior court of the county in which the mine is situated, a petition setting forth the facts. After proper notice and hearing, the court may order judgment vesting the interest of the delinquent in the mine or claim in the petitioner.

Grubstake Contracts

(Chap. 7, Public Resources Code of California)

Sec. 2606.   Recordation of Grubstake Contracts

"All grubstake contracts and prospecting agreements hereafter entered into, and which may in any way affect the title of mining locations, or other locations under the mining laws of this State, shall be void and of no effect unless the instrument has first been recorded in the office of the county recorder of the county in which the instrument is made. The instrument shall be duly acknowledged before a notary public or other person competent to take acknowledgments. Grubstake contracts and prospecting agreements, duly acknowledged and recorded as provided for in this section, shall be prima facie evidence in all courts in this State in all cases wherein the title to mining locations and other locations under the mining laws of this State are in dispute.''

A grubstake, or prospecting contract, as it is sometimes called, is where one of the parties thereto, called the outfitter, is to furnish the other, called the prospector, supplies, money or both, to and while the other is prospecting for and obtaining mineral land, by location, for their joint advantage or in such proportion as may be agreed upon. It is the duty of the prospector to use reasonable diligence and make reasonable exertions in seeking mineral deposits, and within a reasonable time make proper location covering discovery. It does not constitute a mining partnership unless the parties thereto actually engage in the joint working of the property; otherwise, they are tenants in common.

All locations made during the existence of the contract inure to the benefit of each of the parties thereto, whether made in the name of only one of them, or in the name of a third person, at the instigation of either. Where a prospector conceals locations made in his own name, or for him, individually, he holds the title thus acquired, or the property for which it is exchanged or the price for which it is sold as a trustee in bad faith for the use and benefit of the outfitter, and will be compelled to make restitution.

It is essential to a right in mining property acquired under a grubstake contract that such property should be acquired by means of the grubstake furnished and pursuant to such contract.

The contract must be founded upon an adequate consideration, and be just and reasonable; that is, it must not be a hard bargain on the prospector.

Independent Contractor

Where the mine owner retains the right to direct the mode and manner in which the assessment work shall be done for an agreed per diem, the relation of master and servant exists and the employer is liable in damages for injuries which may be sustained by his employee while he is engaged in such employment. But, if work is done under a contract, such as to excavate a tunnel of certain dimensions for an agreed number of lineal feet, or to sink a shaft of a certain size to a certain depth, for an agreed amount, and the mine owner has no right of control as to the mode of doing the work contracted for, the party so doing such work is an independent contractor, and he, and not the mine owner, is liable for such injuries.

Leases

Each mining lease has its own peculiar details. The form of words used is of no consequence. It is the intention of the parties, as expressed in the instrument, and not its form that determines whether it is a lease or a license or a contract for labor. If the contract gives exclusive possession it is a lease; if it merely confers the privilege of occupation, under the owner, it is a license; if it fixes a rule for compensation for services rendered, as, for instance, a share of the profits realized in working the mine, it is a contract for labor. A lease is sometimes coupled with an option to purchase the property leased, in which case they are separate instruments and the option may outlive the lease. Time is always of the essence of both documents whether so expressly stated or not. Where there is any doubt or uncertainty as to the meaning of covenants in such a lease they are construed strongly against the lessor and in favor of the lessee. A covenant to work the property continuously means continuous to the end of the term. A mere covenant to work the property is not tantamount to a covenant to work continuously. If the payment of royalty is provided for, the lessee is bound to proceed with his mining operations with reasonable diligence. The lease is subject to abandonment or forfeiture. A location may be made and leased on the same day. No lease should be for a longer period than twenty-five years. If it be for a period of one year, or less, it need not be in writing. Where there is no agreement in the lease against subletting, the lessee has the right to sublease all or portions of the land for the purpose specified in the lease. A stipulation as to the removal of machinery or other improvements placed by the lessee is controlling. The term ''gross proceeds'' means the entire proceeds of the ore mined, less the cost of sampling, freight, and treatment of the ores.

Mining Partnership
(Chap. 5, Secs. 2351-2360 incl., Public Resources Code of California.)

To constitute a mining partnership, two or more parties must be associated together in the ownership or possession of a mining claim in some way and actually engage in working the same.

The partnership is not dissolved by the death of a partner nor by the sale of a partnership interest. The purchaser, from the date of his purchase, becomes a member of the partnership. The partners are in the relation of trustees for each other. The property worked and the business of the partnership may be controlled by a majority of the members of the partnership acting for the best interest of all concerned. Each partner is jointly liable for the debts of the firm.

As previously suggested, the property worked is not necessarily property owned by the partnership, if it be so, it is subject to the lien of each member of the firm for debt due to himself or to the creditors of the firm. One mining partner may sue his copartner for an accounting. A partner may properly sell his interest at a greater price than that received by the other partners.

Option

An option is a right acquired by contract to accept or reject a present offer within a limited time. It may be coupled with a lease. Time is of the essence of the contract, whether so therein expressed or not. It must be based upon a sufficient consideration; otherwise, it may be withdrawn at any time before acceptance. A consideration of one dollar, in the absence of fraud or bad faith, or the making of expenditures upon the property, as for instance, the performance of the annual assessment work thereon, is a sufficient consideration. After acceptance by the optionee, the parties are mutually bound and the option may be specifically enforced. An option usually is accompanied by the duly executed deed of the optioner, which is placed in escrow to be delivered to the optionee upon his performance of the conditions of the option, or to be returned to the maker in the event of default; in the meantime the title to the property remains in the grantor and subject to claims against him. The deed when delivered will relate back to the date of the escrow agreement and cut off any intervening rights or equities acquired by a third party who had notice of the terms and conditions of the escrow. Hence, the option should be recorded by its holder. At the time the escrow is made, and as a part thereof the option holder properly should execute a quit-claim of the property to the optioner to be delivered to him upon de-fault of the optionee or to the latter upon full compliance with the terms of the option. This is to clear the record title to the property, if there be no conveyance under the terms of the option.

Delivery of the deed by the escrow holder, contrary to instruction, confers no title, particularly as against those who take with notice.

Payment of Wages

The Labor Code, Chapter 1, Article 3, Section 270 (added by Stats. 1945, Ch. 628) provides that:

"No person, or agent or officer thereof, engaged in the business of extracting or of extracting and refining or reducing minerals other than petroleum, except persons having a free and unencumbered title to the fee of the property being worked and except mining partnerships in respect to the members of the partnership, shall fail or neglect, before commencing work in any period for which a single payment of wages is made, to have on hand or on deposit with a bank or trust company, in the county where such property is located or if there is no bank or trust company in the county, then in the bank or trust company nearest the property, cash or readily salable securities of a market value sufficient to pay the wages of every person em-ployed on the mining property, or in connection therewith, for such period.

Any person, or agent or officer thereof, who violates this section is guilty of a misdemeanor."

See also *Independent Contractor,* page 44.

Regulations for Mining Leasing Act Minerals

The Code of Federal Regulations, Title 30, Chapter 2, Part 231 provides operating and safety regulations governing the mining of potash, oil shale, sodium and phosphate, sulfur, gold, silver, or quick-silver, and other nonmetallic minerals including silica sand, on lands or deposits occupied under lease or permit granted in accordance with the Mineral Leasing Act.

Since July 1, 1944, the administration and enforcement of these regulations are vested in the Geological Survey, Department of the Interior. The function of making inspections for the safety and wel-fare of miners under these regulations is vested in the Bureau of Mines, Department of the Interior.

Further information on these regulations as they are supervised in California can be obtained from the office of the Conservation Division, U.S. Geological Survey, Bartlett Building, 215 West 7th Street, Los Angeles.

Tenancy in Common

A tenancy in common arises from the joint location of or ownership in a mining claim and consists of undivided interests therein. The parties thereto are not mining partners unless they work the mine to-gether by agreement. A cotenant who does not exclude his cotenants, may work the mine in the usual way and extract ore therefrom without being chargeable with waste or liable to the other cotenants for damages, and an injunction will not be granted at their instance to prevent the working of the mine.

The operating cotenant works the property at his own expense; he alone must sustain any loss which results from his working the property and he alone is responsible for the debts thereby contracted; he must account to the nonparticipating cotenants for their pro rata share in the net results.

The title of a cotenant may be divested after due notice to contribute his proportion of the annual expenditure, or by the actual adverse possession for the statutory period of the other cotenants, or some of them, evidenced by ouster, or by obtaining a patent from the government in their own names unless the excluded cotenant brings suit to enforce the trust when not barred by laches, the statute of limitations or the rights of third parties without notice. Hence, such excluded cotenant need neither file an adverse nor a protest against such application for patent. A cotenant becomes a trustee for his cotenants when he relocates the claim or permits its relocation by a third person with whom he is in collusion, or obtains a patent in his own name.

A cotenant may maintain an action for the recovery of the claim without joining his cotenants. A cotenant may sell or encumber his undivided interest at pleasure but he cannot sell, lease, or encumber a specific part of the common land.

See also, *Working the Claim,* page 48.

Use of Water

A landowner (including the owner of a valid, unpatented mining claim) has a riparian right to the use of water which flows across, rises upon, or percolates through his land, insofar as this water has not been previously put to beneficial use by legal appropriators or by other riparian owners farther downstream. The landowner can make any reasonable use of such water upon his riparian land, that does not deprive the prior claimant of the quantity and quality of water to which he is entitled. This includes consumptive use of any unclaimed part of the flow. No formality is required for such riparian use.

Where the water does not naturally flow across the land but is brought to it by diversion from an outside point, such appropriation should be made according to state law.

The appropriation of water is discussed in more detail elsewhere in this report. Further questions regarding the use of water should be directed to the State Water Rights Board, 1401 21st Street. P. O. Box 1592, Sacramento 7, California.

If the miner intends to mine by hydraulic methods anyplace in California where the operations drain into any stream tributary to the Sacramento or San Joaquin Rivers, there must be full compliance with the Debris Commission Act (27 Stat. 507, as amended 33 U.S.C.A. 661 et seq.)

This act created the California Debris Commission of three members of the Corps of Engineers, U. S. Army. No hydraulic mining can be carried on in any of the area above described unless and until the operator shall have obtained a permit from the Debris Commission.

The operator must show that he has storage facilities behind some existing debris dam or that he has constructed or can construct ample facilities for restraining all debris from the mining operations from entering the stream.

The forms for filing the petition should be obtained from the Debris Commission office in the Wright Building at the corner of 8th and L Streets in the City of Sacramento, California. Upon filing the petition, if the same is found regular, the Commission shall cause a notice of hearing to be published in some newspaper of general circulation in the community interested in the matter and at the time fixed for the hearing the applicant must be prepared to make a full and complete showing.

A fee will be charged for each cubic yard of material mined by this method. Full particulars and forms may be obtained by application to the Debris Commission at the address given above.

Working the Claim

To work a mining claim is to do something toward making it productive, such as developing or extracting an ore body after it is dicovered.

A mine owner is entitled to work his mining claim in a lawful manner; but no manner can be considered lawful which precludes another from the enjoyment of his rights, if his work in fact injures the property of another, be he ever so cautious or careful to avoid injurious consequences. (For instance, allowing his tailings to flow upon another's land without his consent.) In such case, the trespasser not only loses his title to the tailings but is liable for damages besides.

The word ''shift'' means a set of workmen who work in turn with other shifts, as a night shift. It means, also, a day's work.

See also *Tenancy in Common*, page 46.

FORMS
Form of Affidavit of Annual Labor

State of California ⎱
County of _____ ⎰ ss

_____, being first duly sworn, deposes and says, that at least (*one*) hundred dollars worth of labor was performed (*or improvements made*) between 12 o'clock noon of the first day of September, 19__, and 12 o'clock noon of the first day of September, 19__, upon the _____ mining claim situate in the _____ Mining District, County of _____, State of California. Such expenditure was made by or at the expense of _____, the owner of said claim, for the purpose of complying with the federal and California mining laws pertaining to annual assessment work.

Subscribed and sworn to before me this _____ day of _____, 19__, _____.
Notary Public in and for the County of _____, State of California.
My commission expires _____.

Form of Amended Location Notice

Know all men by these presents, that _____, the undersigned, has this _____ day of _____, 19__, amended, located, and claimed and by these presents does amend, locate, and claim by right of discovery and amended location in compliance with section 2310 of the Public Resources Code of California (*fifteen*) hundred linear feet of the _____ lode, vein, ledge, or deposit along the vein together with (*three*) hundred feet on each side of the middle of the said vein at the surface situate in _____ Mining District, County of _____, State of California, and described as follows: Beginning at corner No. 1, whence (*name some natural object or permanent monu-*

ment) is distant _____ feet in a _____ direction, thence (*northeasterly*) (*fifteen*) hundred feet to corner No. 2, thence (*southeasterly*) (*three*) hundred feet to end center monument, thence (*southeasterly*) (*three*) hundred feet to corner No. 3, thence (*southwesterly*) (*fifteen*) hundred feet to corner No. 4, thence (*northwesterly*) (*three*) hundred feet to end center monument, thence (*northwesterly*) (*three*) hundred feet to point of beginning. This being the same lode originally located on the _____ day of _____, _____, and recorded on the _____ day of _____, _____, in Book _____, page _____ of _____ records in the office of county recorder of said _____ County. This further and amended notice of location is made without waiver of any previously acquired rights, but for the purpose of correcting any errors or defects or ommissions in the original location, description, or record and to secure all the benefits of said section of said Civil Code.

_____, Locator.

The statement about discovery work and marking of lode claims should be used.

Form of Contract

The terms of the agreement made this _____ day of _____, 19__, between _____, party of the first part, and _____, party of the second part, are as follows, viz: That the said party of the second part shall excavate or run _____ lineal feet of tunnel work within the _____ mining claim situate in the _____ Mining District, County of _____ and State of California, commencing at a point to wit: _____ feet (*west*) from the (*east end center monument of said claim*) for the agreed sum or price of _____ dollars per lineal foot; said tunnel to be _____ feet in width and _____ feet in height, in the clear, and to be timbered where necessary. Payment therefor by said party of the first part shall be made in full within _____ days after the full completion of said work. Work upon said tunnel under this contract shall commence within _____ days from the date hereof and the same shall be fully completed in proper and minerlike manner by said party of the second part on or before the thirtieth day of June next thereafter ensuing; said party of the second part to hold said party of the first part harmless as against all and every lien of laborers, miners, and mechanics, and for materials furnished.

In witness whereof the said parties hereto have hereunto, and to its duplicate, set their hands the day and year first above written.

_____

_____

Form of Deed

I, _____, grant (*or quitclaim*) to _____, that certain mining claim situate in the _____ Mining District, County of _____, State of California, and being the _____ mining claim, and more fully described in volume _____, page _____, of the records of (*quartz claims*) records of said county (*or being Mineral Survey No. ___*).

Witness my hand this (*insert day*) of (*insert month*), 19__.

_____.

Short Form of Lease

This agreement of lease made and entered into this _____ day of _____, 19____, by and between _____ and _____ Witnesseth: That the lessor for and in consideration of _____ dollars, cash in hand paid, receipt of which is hereby acknowledged, and of the covenants and agreements hereinafter contained on the part of the lessee to be paid, kept and performed, does grant, convey, demise, and let exclusively unto the said lessee that certain tract of land situate in _____ Mining District, County of _____, State of California, described as follows:

(*Insert description*)

for the sole purpose of exploring, operating and mining precious and other minerals and to sell the products thereof and to pay to the lessor a royalty of _____ percent of the gross proceeds within ten days after the settlement for each clean up.

The lessee agrees to keep said premises free and clear of all costs, leins and encumbrances done, made or suffered by permit, the lessor to place and maintain in a conspicuous place upon said premises such notice as shall be lawfully necessary to protect the lessor against such claims.

All machinery and improvements placed upon said premises by the lessee may be removed by him within _____ days after the termination of this lease.

The lessee hereby agrees to carry a workmen's compensation policy in a responsible company; said policy to be placed in force upon the commencement of said work.

It is agreed that this lease shall remain in force for a term of _____ years from this date.

Witness our hands the day and year first above written.

Form of Lode Location Notice

Notice is hereby given that I, _____, do hereby locate and claim (*fifteen*) hundred linear feet of this vein or lode, together with surface ground extending (*three*) hundred feet in width on each side of the middle of said vein or lode and described as follows: Commencing at a post (*or stone monument*) where this notice is posted, which post (*or stone monument*) is at the point of discovery on said vein or lode and on the center line of this location, I hereby claim (*six*) hundred feet extending in a (*southwesterly*) direction along the course of said vein and (*nine*) hundred feet in a (*northeasterly*) direction. The general course of the vein or lode is (*northeasterly*) and (*southeasterly*) as near as can be determined from present developments. The discovery post (*or stone monument*) is situated about _____ feet from (*name some natural object or permanent monument and give direction*).

The name of this claim is _____ and it is situated in _____ Mining District, County of _____, State of California.

Date _____.   _____, Locator.

Note: (*No witness required.*)

(*The post must be not less than four inches in diameter and the stone monument must be at least eighteen inches high.*)

This diagram is intended to give a general ideal plan of location.

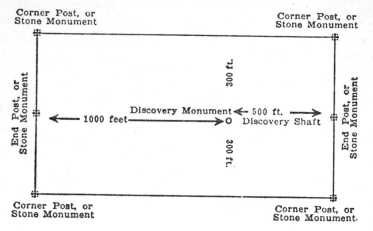

The state law now requires that the location notice shall contain a statement that the boundaries have been marked and discovery work has been done as specified in the statute.

The following form is suggested and may be filled out and attached to the location notice unless printed location blanks provide for these statements.*

NOTICE IS HEREBY GIVEN by the undersigned Locator__ of the within described Lode Mining Claim, in accordance with the provisions of Chapter 644 of the Statutes of 1941 which amends Section 2313 of the Public Resources Code of the State of California relating to mining claims, that there has been erected

---

* Also see statement on page 23 regarding preferable method of recording claim and performance of discovery work.

at the discovery point, at each corner and at the center of each end line of the said claim, a post not less than four (4) inches in diameter or a stone monument, at least eighteen (18) inches high.

That there has been sunk a discovery shaft upon said claim at least ten (10) feet deep measured from the lowest point of the rim _____; a tunnel _____;
                                                      (Yes or No)   (Yes or No)
adit _____; open cut _____; upon said claim to at least ten (10) feet
  (Yes or No)   (Yes or No)
below the surface.

That the discovery work indicated above has been completed within ninety (90) days from the date of location of said claim.

Dated_____, 19____.
                                         Locator _____
                                         _____
                                         _____

Note: Mark one of the above to indicate how discovery work was done. This may be NEW work or extension of OLD shaft, adit, tunnel or open cut.

A location of either Lode or Placer mining claim is null and void unless such DISCOVERY work is duly performed and a true copy of Location Notice recorded within ninety (90) days from date of location.

Annual ASSESSMENT work must also be performed within one year after the following first day of September from date of location.

Form of Mill-Site Location Notice

Notice is hereby given that I, _____, proprietor of that certain vein or lode or placer claim known as the _____ mining claim (or the owner of that certain quartz mill or reduction works known as the_____) have this _____ day of _____, 19___, located five acres of nonmineral land to be known as the _____ mill site, situate in _____Mining District, County of _____, State of California, and described as follows: Commencing at a point from which (name natural object or permanent monument) bears _____, feet; thence (south) seven hundred and twenty-six feet; thence (west) three hundred feet; thence (north) seven hundred and twenty-six feet; thence (east) three hundred feet to the point of beginning.

Name of this mill site is_____.
                                         _____, Locator.

Note: (No witnesses required.)

Form of Notice of Nonresponsibility for Labor or Materials Furnished

Notice is hereby given to all persons, that the undersigned _____ is the owner of _____ mine (or mining claims) hereinafter described, with all the improvements thereon. That said mine (or mining claims) now is in the possession of and is being worked and operated by _____, pursuant to a contract (or option to purchase, or lease) made and executed by the undersigned in favor of said _____, dated _____ 19___, said contract (or option to purchase, or lease) to be in force up to and including _____ 19___.

The undersigned is not working nor operating said mine (or mining claims), nor any portion thereof, and does not intend to work or operate said mine (or mining claims), nor any part thereof, nor purchase any supplies or materials therefor, during the life of said contract (or option to purchase, or lease) with said _____.

The name of said mine (or mining claims) is _____ and is situate, lying and being in _____ Mining District, County of _____, State of California. The notice of location of said mine (or mining claims) being duly recorded in Book _____, at page _____, of the records of said _____ county in the office of the county recorder of said county to which said record reference is hereby made for a more particular description of said mine (or mining claims).

In witness whereof, the said _____ has hereunto set his hand this _____ day of _____, 19___.

State of California ⎱
County of_____ ⎰ ss.

_____, being first duly sworn, according to law, deposes and says: That he is the owner of the premises particularly mentioned and described in the foregoing Notice of Nonresponsibility for Labor or Materials Furnished. That he has read the same and knows the contents thereof. That the same is true of his own knowledge. Subscribed and sworn to before me this _____ day of _____, 19___.

_____

Notary Public in and for the County of_____,
State of California.

My commission expires _____.

NOTE.—This notice must be posted in a conspicuous place upon the property within ten days after the owner (or person having or claiming interest therein) has obtained knowledge of construction, alteration or repair work or labor upon such property and he should file for record a verified copy of said notice in the office of the proper county recorder. The foregoing verification may be made by any one having knowledge of the facts, on behalf of the owner or person for whose protection the notice is given.

Short Form of Option

In consideration of the sum of _____ dollars, to me in hand paid, I, the undersigned, will sell to _____ my certain mining claim known as _____ situate in _____ Mining District, County of _____ and State of _____ for the sum of _____ dollars, at any time within _____ months from date, payable as follows, to wit: _____.

Upon full payment made I will convey said mining claim to said optionee by a good and sufficient deed.

The right of entry and possession of said premises is hereby given to said optionee together with the right to extract ore therefrom, but with no right thereto or removal thereof, unless and until this option be consummated according to its terms.

All work done upon said mining claim by said optionee shall be done in a miner-like manner and at the sole cost and expense of the optionee. Actual work upon said premises to commence on _____ and to proceed with reasonable diligence unless prevented by strikes, the elements, unavoidable accidents or other causes beyond the control of the optionee.

The optionee shall keep said premises free and clear of all costs, liens and encumbrances done, made or suffered by him—and see that the notice of nonresponsibility which may be posted by the optioner upon said premises to protect the same from such liens, is kept in place.

The optionee hereby agrees to carry workmen's compensation insurance in a responsible company, said policy to be placed in force immediately upon the commencement of said work.

The optionee shall and will quietly and peaceably quit and surrender said premises and any ore extracted by him therefrom upon the termination of this option from any legal cause.

Upon the failure to make any payments herein provided for upon said purchase price of said premises at the time herein specified for the same to be made, the right of the optionee shall immediately cease and determine and the payments theretofore made by him shall immediately become the property of the optioner, and the optionee hereby waives all claim thereto.

All machinery and improvements placed upon said premises by the optionee may be removed by him within _____ days after the termination of this option.

Witness my hand this _____ day of _____.

_____

Form of Placer Location Notice (on Surveyed Land)

Notice is hereby given that the undersigned has this _____ day of _____, 19__, located a placer mining claim situate on public surveyed land in _____ Mining District, County of _____, State of California, described as follows: The ____ of section _____, in township _____, range _____, M. D. M., containing _____ acres.

This claim shall be known as the _____ placer mining claim.

_____, Locator.

Note: (*No witnesses required.*)

Form of Placer Location Notice (on Unsurveyed Land)

Notice is hereby given that I, _____, have this _____ day of _____, 19__, located on public unsurveyed lands in the _____ Mining District, County of _____, State of California, a placer claim described as follows: Beginning at a (tree, rock in place, stone, post or monument) upon which is posted the notice of location, running thence (north) six hundred and sixty feet to a post marked _____, thence (east) thirteen hundred and twenty feet to a post marked _____, thence (south) six hundred and sixty feet to a post marked _____, thence (west) thirteen hundred and twenty feet to place of beginning; containing twenty acres.

All of said posts are at least four inches in diameter and set at least one foot in the ground and surrounded by a mound of stone.

This location is situated about (feet) distant from (name some natural object or permanent monument).

The name of this claim is _____.

_____, Locator.

Note: (*No witnesses required.*)

In some cases, printed location notice forms may be purchased which carry the necessary form to be filled out, showing the performance of discovery work required under state law, (Secs. 2304, 2305, cited above). If these are not available, the following form may be used and attached to the location notice.*

Form to Be Attached to PLACER LOCATION NOTICE when recorded:

NOTICE IS HEREBY GIVEN by the undersigned Locator__ of the within described Placer Mining Claim, in accordance with the provisions of Chapter 644 of the Statutes of 1941, which amends Section 2313 of the Public Resources Code of the State of California relating to mining claims:

That there has been sunk a discovery shaft upon said claim at least ten (10) feet deep measured from the lowest point of the rim _____; a tunnel _____;
(Yes or No)   (Yes or No)
adit _____ upon said claim to at least ten (10) feet below the surface, or an
(Yes or No)
open cut _____ from which cut there has been removed not less than seven
(Yes or No)
(7) cubic yards of material.

That the discovery work indicated above has been completed within ninety (90) days from the date of location of said claim.

Dated _____ 19____.   Locator _____
_____
_____

Note: Mark one of the above to indicate how discovery work was done. This may be NEW work or extension of OLD shaft, adit, tunnel or open cut.

A location of either Lode or Placer mining claim is null and void unless such DISCOVERY work is duly performed and a true copy of Location Notice recorded within ninety (90) days from date of location.

Annual ASSESSMENT work must also be performed within one year after the following first day of September from date of location.

The above form of statement has been suggested as meeting the requirements of Chapter 644 of the Statutes of 1941 which amends Section 2313 of the Public Resources Code, relative to the recording of mining location notices.

Form of Tunnel Site Location Notice

Notice is hereby given that I, _____, have this _____ day of _____, 19__, located a tunnel site to be known as the _____ tunnel claim, situate in _____ Mining District, County of _____, State of California, and described as follows: Commencing at this notice of location which is posted at the face or point of commencement of this tunnel and situate about ____ feet from a (*blazed tree*) _____ inches in diameter, marked _____ (*or some other natural object or permanent monument*). The boundary lines of said tunnel site are marked by (*stakes or monuments*) placed along said lines at an interval of not more than six hundred feet from the face or point of commencement of the tunnel to the terminus of three thousand feet therefrom.

_____, Locator.

Note: (*No witnesses required.*)

* Also see statement on page 23 regarding preferable method of recording claim and performance of discovery work.

MINERAL PATENTS

CONTENTS

PROCEDURE FOR OBTAINING PATENT TO A MINING CLAIM

Deposits of minerals. other than coal, oil, gas, oil shale, sodium, phosphate and potash (sulfur in Louisiana and New Mexico) in both surveyed and unsurveyed lands belonging to the United States are open to exploration and purchase under the mining laws of May 10, 1872. The lands in which the minerals are found are open to occupation and purchase by citizens of the United States or those who have declared their intentions to become citizens, under regulations prescribed by the Secretary of the Interior, and according to the local customs or rules of miners in the several mining districts, so far as they are applicable and not inconsistent with the laws of the United States. Certain minerals belonging to the United States (coal, oil, gas, oil shale, sodium, potash, phosphate, and in Louisiana and New Mexico, sulfur) may be acquired under what are known as the mineral leasing laws and are not subject to location and purchase under the mining laws. Information regarding the acquisition of any of these leasable minerals will be furnished upon request.

Under the provisions of the mining laws, the locator or owner of a valid mining location has the right to the exclusive possession for mining purposes of the land embraced in the location, and may continue to hold such possession so long as he performs labor or makes improvements of not less than $100 in value on or for the benefit of the claim each assessment year. Upon failure to comply with the assessment work requirement during any year, the claim is open to relocation at any time prior to the resumption of work by the owner, or his heirs, legal representatives or assigns. Thus, while a valid mining claim may be held and mined under the location title, that title may be lost by failure to perform the required annual assessment work, and for this reason it is desirable to obtain a patent for the claim, after which annual assessment work is no longer required. Before a patent can be obtained, not less than $500 must have been expended in labor or improvements in the development of the claim.

The procedure for obtaining patent to a mining claim is briefly set forth herein for the benefit of locators and owners of such claims.

The following is reprinted merely as an outline or as preliminary information for the holder of a mining location who desires to obtain a patent. Being merely general information, the prospector or miner should not take it as a full course in mining law practice. A person untrained in the intricacies of practice before the Bureau of Land Management should never attempt to file and prosecute an application for patent. Before undertaking patent proceedings, consult a person experienced in the practice before the Bureau of Land Management.

Lode Claims *

1. The claim must be surveyed by a U.S. Mineral Surveyor. An application to have the survey made must be filed with the District Cadastral Engineer.

2. Formal notice of the application must be given by posting a copy of the plat of survey and a notice of application for patent on the claim.

3. A proper application for patent must be filed in the land office (list appended hereto), supported by the following papers:
   (a) Two (2) copies of the field notes and two (2) copies of plats of survey.
   (b) Proof of posting the plat and notice on the claim.
   (c) Abstract of title or proof of possessory right to and including date of filing application.
   (d) Proof of citizenship.
   (e) Proof of improvements.
   (f) Payment of filing fee.
   (g) Publisher's agreement.
   (h) Notice for publication.
   (i) Notice for posting in land office.

4. Final proceedings.
   (a) Proof of publication must be made.
   (b) Proof of continuous posting of plat and notice on claim during full 60-day period of publication must be made.
   (c) Statement that all fees and charges have been paid must be filed.
   (d) An application to purchase accompanied by tender of purchase price must be filed.
   (e) Diligence.

1. Survey

Claimant must apply to the Office Cadastral Engineer for authority to survey the claim (list appended hereto). Form of application may be obtained from that office. Deposit of a sum estimated by that officer as sufficient to cover cost of making plats and field notes must be made before survey will be authorized. Applicant will, by private contract, arrange with a United States mineral surveyor to make the survey. The applicant may obtain from the Office Cadastral Engineer a list of United States mineral surveyors from which he can select one to employ to survey his claim.

* The above paragraphs 1, 2, and 3 have been changed to conform to later provisions covering mining applications for patent.

2. Posting on Claim

After the survey, applicant will post a copy of the plat and a notice of intention to apply for a patent in a conspicuous place on the claim, or on one of a group of claims, where it can be readily seen by any interested party.

3. Application for Patent

The application and accompanying documents must show that the applicant has the right of possession to the claim and applicant should state briefly but clearly the facts constituting the basis of his right to a patent, a full description of the vein or lode, whether ore has been extracted, and, if so, of what amount and value, and the precise place within the limits of each claim where the vein or lode is exposed.

In addition to the improvements mentioned in the field notes, it is proper that the claimant in his application for patent should describe in detail the shafts, cuts, tunnels, or other workings claimed as improvements, giving their dimensions, value, and the course and distance thereof to the nearest corner of the public surveys. This statement of the description and value of the improvements must be supported by the statements of two disinterested witnesses.

Application must be filed in duplicate and all supporting statements must be signed in the land district and the affidavit of the publisher may be verified before any officer authorized to administer oaths within the land district where the claim is situated. Individual claimants must sign application, except that if claimant is absent from district, the application must be signed by an attorney in fact within the land district. Application by a corporation may be signed by its officers, or by an agent or attorney in fact who has been duly authorized.*

The application for patent will be filed in the land office† after plat and notice have been posted on the claim and must be supported by:

(a) Two (2) copies of the field notes and two (2) copies of plats of survey.

(b) Proof of posting on claim. The statement of two credible witnesses, not claimants or their attorneys in fact, giving date and place of posting, with copy of notice attached to the statement.

(c) Abstract or certificate of title. The application for patent must be supported by a certified copy of each original and amended location notice and also by an abstract or a certificate of title of each claim, brought down to a date reasonably near date of filing the application, and must be supplemented later to include date of filing of the application, and must be submitted in such form and by such Abstracter or title Company as may be satisfactory to the Director of the Bureau of Land Management.

Proof of possessory title. As to old claims, where the records have been lost or destroyed and where all controversy over the claims has long since ceased, applicant may furnish a certified copy of the statute

---

* Authority of attorney in fact. (*a*) Attorney for individual shown by original or certified copy of power of attorney. (*b*) Attorney for corporation shown by certified copy of resolution appointing or authorizing official to appoint, with original or certified copy of power of attorney in the latter case.

† If there is no land office in the state in which the claim is situated the application should be filed with the proper Regional Administrator except in the states of Arkansas, Florida, Louisiana and Mississippi. In those states the application should be filed with the Director, Bureau of Land Management, Washington 25, D. C.

of limitations, applicable to mining claims in the state, with his statement supported by those of disinterested persons, showing the facts as to the origin and maintenance of his title, the area of the claim, the kind and extent of mining improvements, whether his title has been disputed in court proceedings or otherwise, with details, as well as any other matters known to him which bear upon his right of possession. A certificate, under seal, by the clerk of the court having jurisdiction, that no action involving right of possession to the claim is pending and that there has been no litigation in the court affecting the title to the claim for the time fixed by the statute of limitations in the state other than has been decided in favor of the applicant for patent, must be filed.

(d) *Proof of citizenship.* Statements of citizenship may be signed either within or without the land district: (1) Of a native-born citizen, by his statement of that fact. (2) Of one who has declared his intention to become a citizen, or has been naturalized, his statement showing date, place and the court before which he declared his intention or from which his naturalization papers issued, and the number of certificate if known. (3) Of an association, competent evidence as above of each member. (4) Of a corporation, by a certified copy of its charter, or certificate of incorporation.

(e) *Proof of improvements.*

(f) *Payment of filing fee.*

(g) *Publisher's agreement.*

(h) *Notice for publication.* At the expense of applicant in a newspaper designated by the Manager; (a) in weekly paper, nine consecutive insertions; (b) in daily paper, nine consecutive Wednesday insertions. Sample form containing essential data is appended.

(i) *Notice for posting in land office.*

4. Final Proceedings

(a) *Proof of publication.* The sworn statement of the publisher that the notice was published for the stated period, giving the first and last dates of the publication.

(b) *Proof of continuous posting.* The statement of the *applicant or his duly authorized attorney in fact* that the plat and notice remained conspicuously posted on the claim during the entire period of publication, giving dates. Where publication is had in nine consecutive issues of a weekly paper or on nine consecutive Wednesdays in a daily paper, the 60-day period does not end until the close of the fourth day after the date of the ninth issue and the plat and notice must remain posted the full 60-day period and the statement must cover that period.

(c) *Proof of fees and charges paid.* Statement of claimant or attorney in fact that all fees and charges have been paid, itemizing them.

(d) *Payment of purchase price.* The purchase price for lode claims of $5 for each acre or fraction thereof must be paid.

(e) *Diligence.* Application must be completed within a reasonable time and failure to do so will result in its rejection.

The cost of obtaining a patent will vary in every case and includes the deposit with the Office Cadastral Engineer to cover office work in connection with the survey, the amount agreed upon by the applicant and the mineral surveyor for surveying the claim, a filing fee of $10 to be paid to the Manager when the application for patent is filed, the cost of furnishing an abstract or a certificate of title of the claims applied for, the charge of the newspaper for publishing the notice of application, and the payment of the purchase price for the land to the Manager when the proofs are completed and the application to purchase the claim is made. There will also be some incidental expense including the cost of the employment of an attorney to look after the patent proceedings whose fee must be considered in determining the cost of obtaining patent for a claim.

The applicant should consult the officials in the land office and the Office Cadastral Engineers concerning any matters about which he may not be fully informed.

Mill Sites

Lands entered as mill sites may be for an area of not more than 5 acres for each mill site and must be shown to be nonmineral in character and not contiguous to a vein or lode. It has been held that a mill site may contact a side line of a lode claim, provided it is shown that the lode or vein does not extend into any part of the ground covered by the mill site. It must be used or occupied for mining or milling purposes. A mill site application may be filed at the same time an application for a patent is filed for adjacent lode claims or the owner of a quartz mill or reduction works, not owning a mine in connection therewith, may receive a patent for a mill site.

A mill site may be located in connection with a placer mining location.

The procedure to be followed in securing a patent for a mill site is the same as that for obtaining a patent for a lode claim except where an application for a mill site is filed at the same time a copy of the application together with a copy of the plat must be posted on the mill site as well as on the lode claims. Where an application is filed for a patent to a mill site only, a copy of the notice of the application and a copy of the plat must be posted on the claim. In lieu of discovery proof of the nonmineral character of the lands must be established and in lieu of improvements, use and occupancy of the land for mill site purposes must be shown; these proofs to be supported by the statements of two or more persons cognizant of the facts.

Placer Claims

1. A mineral survey must be made of placer claims on unsurveyed lands or on surveyed lands when the land cannot be described in terms of the public land survey.

2. Formal notice of the application must be given by posting a notice of intention to apply for a patent on the claim, and, if a mineral survey has been made, a copy of the plat must also be posted.

3. A proper application for patent must be filed in the land office (list appended hereto), supported by the following papers.
   (a) Copy of the field notes and plat of survey.
   (b) Proof of posting the plat and notice on the claim.
   (c) Abstract of title or proof of possessory right.
   (d) Proof of citizenship.
   (e) Proof of improvements.
   (f) Payment of filing fee.

(g) Publisher's agreement.
(h) Notice for publication.
(i) Notice for posting in land office.
(j) Proof of no known veins.

4. Final proceedings.
(a) Proof of publication must be made.
(b) Proof of continuous posting of plat and notice on claim during full 60-day period of publication must be made.
(c) Statement that all fees and charges have been paid must be filed.
(d) An application to purchase accompanied by tender of purchase price must be filed at rate of $2.50 per acre or fraction thereof.
(e) Diligence.

1. Survey

When applying for patent to placer claims on unsurveyed lands or on surveyed lands when the land applied for cannot be described in terms of the public land survey, it will be necessary to have a mineral survey made of the claims.* Claimant must apply to the Office Cadastral Engineer for authority to survey the claim (list appended). Form of application may be obtained from his office. Deposit of a sum estimated by that officer sufficient to cover cost of making plats and field notes must be made before survey will be authorized. Applicant will, by private contract, arrange with a United States mineral surveyor to make the survey. The applicant may obtain from the Office Cadastral Engineer a list of United States mineral surveyors from which he can select one to employ to survey his claim.

2. Posting on Claim

Applicant will post notice of intention to apply for a patent on the claim, and, if a mineral survey has been made, a copy of the plat must also be posted.

3. Application for Patent

The application must show that applicant has the right of possession to the claim and applicant should state briefly but clearly the facts constituting the basis of his right to a patent and such data as will support the claim that the land applied for is placer ground containing valuable deposits not in vein or lode formation and that title is sought, not to control water courses or to obtain valuable timber, but in good faith because of the mineral therein. This statement, of course, must depend upon the character of the deposit and the natural features of the ground, but the following details should be covered as fully as possible: If the claim is for a deposit of placer gold, there must be stated the yield per pan, or cubic yard, as shown by prospecting and development work, distance to bedrock, formation and extent of the deposit, and all other facts upon which he bases his allegation that the claim is valuable for its deposits of placer gold. If it is a building stone or deposit other than gold claimed under the placer laws, he must describe fully

* Where placer claims are upon surveyed lands and conform to legal subdivisions, no further survey or plat is required.

the amount, nature and extent of the deposits, stating the reasons he regards it as valuable mineral claim. He will also be required to describe fully the natural features of the claim; streams, if any, must be fully described as to their course, amount of water carried, and fall within the claim; and he must state kind and amount of timber and other vegetation thereon and adaptability to mining or other uses. All mining improvements must be tied to a section or quarter section corner of the public land survey.

If the claim is all placer ground, that fact must be stated in the application and supported by accompanying proofs; if of mixed placer and lode, it should be so set out, with a description of all known lodes situated within the boundaries of the claim. A specific declaration must be furnished for each lode intended to be claimed. In all cases, whether the lode is claimed or excluded, it must be surveyed and marked upon the plat, the field notes and plat giving the area of the lode claim or claims and the area of the placer separately. All other known lodes are, by the silence of the applicant, excluded by law from all claim by him, of whatsoever nature, possessory or otherwise.

Since no examination and report by a mineral surveyor are available in cases of claims taken by legal subdivisions, the claimant, in his application, should describe in detail the shafts, cuts, tunnels, or other workings claimed as improvements, giving their dimensions, value and the course and distance thereof to the nearest corner of the public surveys in addition to the data above required. This statement of the description and value of the improvements must be supported by the statements of two disinterested witnesses.

The application for patent must be filed in duplicate and all supporting statements must be signed in the land district and the affidavit of the publisher may be verified before an officer authorized to administer oaths within the land district where the claim is situated. Individual claimants must sign the application, except that if claimant is absent from the district, the application must be signed by an attorney in fact within the land district. Application by a corporation may be signed by its officers, or by an agent or attorney in fact, who has been duly authorized.[*]

The application must be filed in the land office after notice of application for patent, together with a copy of the plat if a mineral survey has been posted on the claim, and must be supported by:

(a) Copy of the field notes and plat of survey.

(b) Proof of posting on claim. The statements of two credible witnesses, not claimants or their attorneys in fact, giving date and place of posting, with copy of notice attached to the statement.

(c) Abstract or certificate of title. The application for patent must be supported by a certified copy of each location notice and also by an abstract or a certificate of title of each claim, brought down to a date reasonably near date of filing the application, and must be supplemented later to include date of filing of application, and must be submitted in such form and by such Abstracter or title Company as may be satisfactory to the Director of the Bureau of Land Management.

---

[*] Authority of attorney in fact. (a) Attorney for individual shown by original or certified copy of power of attorney. (b) Attorney for corporation shown by certified copy of resolution appointing or authorizing official to appoint, with original or certified copy of power of attorney in the latter case.

Proof of possessory title. As to old claims, where the records have been lost or destroyed, and where all controversy over the claims has long since ceased, applicant may furnish a certified copy of the statute of limitations applicable to mining claims in the State, with his statement supported by those of disinterested persons, showing the facts as to the origin and maintenance of his title, the area of the claim, the amount and extent of mining improvements, whether his title has been disputed in court proceedings or otherwise, with details, as well as any other matters known to him which bear upon his right of possession. A certificate, under seal, by the clerk of the court having jurisdiction, that no action involving right of possession to the claim is pending and that there has been no litigation in the court affecting the title to the claim for the time fixed by the statute of limitations in the State other than has been decided in favor of the applicant for patent, must be filed.

(d) Proof of citizenship. Statements of citizenship may be signed either within or without the land district: (1) of a native-born citizen, by his verified statement of that fact. (2) Of one who has declared his intention to become a citizen, or has been naturalized, his statement showing date, place, and, the court before which he declared his intention, or from which his naturalization papers issued, and the number of certificate, if known. Of an association, competent evidence as above of each member. (3) Of a corporation, by a certified copy of its charter or certificate of incorporation.

(e) Proof of improvements.

(f) Payment of filing fee.

(g) Publisher's agreement.

(h) Notice for publication. At the expense of applicant in a newspaper designated by the Manager; (a) in weekly paper, nine consecutive insertions; (b) in daily paper, nine consecutive Wednesday insertions. Sample form containing essential data appended.

(i) Notice for posting in land office.

(j) Proof of no known veins.

4. Final Proceedings

(a) Proof of publication. The sworn statement of the publisher that the notice was published for the stated period, giving the first and last dates of the publication.

(b) Proof of continuous posting. The statement of the *applicant or his duly authorized attorney in fact* that the plat and notice remained continuously posted on the claim during the entire period of publication, giving dates. Where publication is had in nine consecutive issues of a weekly paper or on nine consecutive Wednesdays in a daily paper, the 60-day period does not end until the close of the fourth day after the date of the ninth issue and the plat and notice must remain posted the full 60-day period and the statement cover that period.

(c) Proof of fees and charges paid. Statement of claimant or attorney in fact that all fees and charges have been paid, itemizing them.

(d) Payment of purchase price. The purchase price for placer claims of $2.50 for each acre or fraction thereof must be paid.

(e) Diligence. Applications must be completed within a reasonable time and failure to do so will result in their rejection.

The cost of obtaining a patent will vary in every case and includes the deposit with the Office Cadastral Engineer to cover office work in connection with the survey, the amount agreed upon by the applicant and the mineral surveyor for surveying the claim, a filing fee of $10 to be paid to the Manager when the application for patent is filed, the cost of furnishing an abstract of title of the claims applied for, the charge of the newspaper for publishing the notice of application, and the payment of the purchase price for the land to the Manager when the proofs are completed and the application to purchase the claim is made. There will also be some incidental expense including the cost of the employment of an attorney to look after the patent proceedings whose fee must be considered in determining the cost of obtaining patent for a claim.

The applicant should consult the officials in the land office and the Office Cadastral Engineer concerning any matters about which he may not be fully informed.

Adverse Claims

Adverse claims must be filed within the 60-day period of publication. (In Alaska, eight months' additional time is allowed beyond the 60-day period.) The claims must be filed by claimant or attorney in fact (with proof of authority) within the land district, must set forth the nature and extent of the conflict, and the interest of the adverse claimant with certified copy of location certificate. Abstract of title prepared by an abstracter who may be satisfactory to the Director of the Bureau of Land Management, and other necessary papers must be filed. Unless the claim is described by legal subdivisions, a plat showing the extent and boundaries of the claim and the conflict must be filed.

Suit must be commenced in a court of competent jurisdiction to determine the right of possession, within 30 days (in Alaska within 60 days) from the date of filing of the adverse claim, and it must be diligently prosecuted to final judgment.

Upon the filing of an adverse claim and commencement of suit, all proceedings in the land office will be stayed until the controversy shall be settled or the adverse claim waived.

A copy of the judgment roll, certified by the clerk of court of his certificate that suit has been dismissed or withdrawn is required as proof of termination of suit.

Sample Form of Notice for Publication

It is expected that these notices shall not be so abbreviated as to curtail the description essential to a perfect notice, and on the other hand that they shall not be of unnecessary length. The printed matter must be set solid without paragraphing or any display in the heading and shall be in the usual body type used in legal notices. If other type is used, no allowance will be made for additional space on that account. The number of solid lines only used in advertising by actual count will be allowed. All abbreviations and copy must be strictly followed. The following is a sample of advertisement set up in accordance with Government requirements and contains all the essential data necessary for publication:

M. A. No. 0353715 Land Office, Sacramento, California, February 15, 1960. Notice is hereby given that Mary L. Murray, whose address is 6920 Blue Hill Drive, Quincy, California, has made application for mineral patent to the

Alexander, Two Pagans, Mary L., Sterling and Little Jim Lode Mining Claims, and Numbers One, Two, Three and Four Mill Sites, all under Mineral Survey No. 6043 A. & B., for lands described as follows, to-wit: Mining Claims: Commencing at Cor. No. 1 of the Sterling Lode Mining Claim, U. S. Mineral Survey No. 9910 A and B., whence the S. ¼ Cor. Sec. 28, T. 3 N., R. 14 W., S. B. M. bears S. 2° 44' W., 778.0 ft.; thence N. 29° 36' W. 1094.3 ft.; thence N. 1° 19' E. 466.3 ft.; thence N. 60° 24' E. 360.4 ft.; thence N. 11° 31' W., 1100.0 ft.; thence N. 10° 41' W., 1500.0 ft.; thence N. 60° 24' E. 16.2 ft.; thence N. 25° 13' W. 1047.9 ft.; thence N. 60° 24' E. 525.0 ft.; thence S. 29° 25' E. 1044.9 ft.; thence N. 60° 24' E. 16.2 ft.; thence S. 10° 41' E. 1500.0 ft.; thence S. 9° 51' E. 1111.0 ft.; thence S. 29° 13' E. 1494.4 ft.; thence S. 60° 24' W. 1190.0 ft. to the place of beginning. Exclusive of conflict with Rice & McAnany No. 2 and Rice & McAnany No. 3 Lodes of Survey No. 5490. Mill Sites: Commencing at Cor. No. 1 of Number Two Millsite, U. S. Mineral Survey No. 9910 A. & B., whence the S. ¼ Cor. Sec. 28, T. 3 N., R. 14 W., S. B. M. bears S. 23° 54' W. 628.3 ft.; thence N. 33° 10' E., 600 ft.; thence S. 56° 50' E. 1452.0 ft.; thence S. 33° 10' W. 342.3 ft.; thence N. 39° 53' W., 472.5 ft.; thence N. 56° 50' W., 1055.9 ft. to the place of beginning. Location notices are recorded as follows—all "Official Records" of Plumas County, California, except as otherwise noted: Alexander, Book 1318, p. 98; amended location, Book 7436, p. 94; Two Pagans, Book 1328, p. 80; amended location, Book 7458, p. 35; Mary L., Book 1328, p. 80; amended location, Book 8893, p. 390; Sterling, Book 49, p. 215 of Mining locations, amended location, Book 7446, p. 85; Little Jim, Book 1328, p. 79; amended location, Book 5174, p. 310; Mill Sites as follows: No. 1, Book 5807, p. 113; No. 2, Book 5731, p. 366; No. 3, Book 5731, P. 367; No. 4 Book 5609, p. 135. Conflicting claims in addition to those mentioned above: Cloud No. 2 Lode, Survey No. 8956 and Little Jim Lode, Survey No. 8879. No other adjoining claims. Walter E. Beck, Manager.

U. S. BUREAU OF LAND MANAGEMENT

District Land Offices

Arizona
1305 North Central Ave., P. O. Box 148, Phoenix

California
Federal and Courthouse Building, Sacramento
1414 8th St., P.O. Box 723, Riverside

Nevada
50 Ryland Street, P. O. Box 1551, Reno

Oregon
1001 N. E. 6th Ave., P. O. Box 3861, Portland 8

In all District Land Offices records are open to the public from 10 a.m. to 3 p.m. Monday through Friday, except holidays.

Cadastral Engineers Offices

Arizona
1305 North Central Ave., P. O. Box 148, Phoenix

California
Federal and Courthouse Building, Sacramento 14

Nevada
50 Ryland Street, P. O. Box 1551, Reno

Oregon
1001 N. E. 6th Ave., P. O. Box 3861, Portland 8

MINERAL PATENTS AND FISSIONABLE SOURCE MATERIALS*

Section 185.54 (of Code of Federal Regulations, Title 43, Chapter I, part 185) is amended by adding thereto the following paragraph:

Every application for patent, based on a mining claim located after August 1, 1946, shall state whether the claimant has or has not had any direct or indirect part in the development of the atomic bomb project.

---

* From U. S. Bureau of Land Management Circular No. 1658, October 13, 1947.

The application must set forth in detail the exact nature of the claimant's participation in the project, and must also state whether as a result of such participation he acquired any confidential, official information as to the existence of deposits of uranium, thorium, or other fissionable source materials in the lands covered by his application. (R.S. 453, 2478; 43 U.S.C. 2, 1201).

For definition of fissionable source materials, see Atomic Energy Commission's regulation, 11 CFR 40.2 (12 F.R. 1855, March 10, 1947).

MINING CLAIMS IN NATIONAL FORESTS OF THE CALIFORNIA REGION *

National Forests were established for the improvement and protection of forests and watersheds. Their administration and management are for use, enjoyment and benefit of all; and the production of timber, water, minerals, forage and other resources.

Generally speaking vacant national forest land in California is open to prospecting and location for mining purposes under the general mining laws of the United States; exceptions being limited acreages that are withdrawn for mining, that have mineral rights outstanding or that were purchased under the Weeks Act or other specific authority. The Secretary of the Interior is authorized to permit prospecting, development, and utilization of mineral resources on Weeks Land when advised by the Secretary of Agriculture that same will not interfere with the purposes for which the land was acquired.

In keeping with the policy of the United States Government to recognize the right of discoverers of locatable mineral deposits to appropriate for mining purposes the ground embracing their discoveries, the Forest Service permits bona fide prospecting and mining on the national forests.** Certain minerals (Mineral Leasing Act of February 20, 1920 as amended) and materials (Mineral Materials Act of July 31, 1947 as amended) are not subject to location. Ordinarily where claims are established, no mineral examination is made until application for patent is filed.

However, in instances where claims are in material conflict with the public interest or interfere with national forest administration and management they are investigated and where facts warrant, their validity is contested. Similar investigation and action is undertaken of claims on which cabins are built and/or the claimant's use and activities are not authorized by mining laws.

Persons entering upon national forests for proper purposes, including prospecting for and locating, developing, mining and processing mineral deposits, must comply with federal, state, county, and local laws including the rules and regulations of the national forests. Information as to whether a specific tract of land is open to the operation of the general mining laws may be obtained from the District Land Office of the district within which the tract is situated. Such information is also generally available at the office of the Regional Forester in San Francisco, Forest Supervisors, and District Rangers. In California, with its long dry season, much attention is given to fire prevention through control of access during critical time and control of use of explosives and fire permits.

Use of national forest land, including that embraced within a valid mining claim, not provided by law requires the securing of a special

---

* Statement from Regional Office, U. S. Forest Service, San Francisco.
** These statements are not concurred in by the revisor, Charles L. Gilmore. See paragraph D, Appendix II, pages 116-117, for additional comment.

use permit or other form of authorization in advance. Unauthorized occupancy and use constitutes a trespass.

Application for various use permits and for purchase of national forest products should be filed with the district ranger or forest supervisor of the particular district or forest involved.

National Forests in California.

Name	Headquarters
Angeles	115 South Los Robles Ave., Pasadena, Calif.
Cleveland	1196 Broadway, San Diego 1, Calif.
Eldorado	Government Center Building, Placerville, Calif.
Inyo	P. O. Box 605, Bishop, Calif.
Klamath	Yreka, Calif.
Lassen	Susanville, Calif.
Los Padres	Federal Building, Santa Barbara, Calif.
Mendocino	Willows, Calif.
Modoc	Alturas, Calif.
Plumas	Quincy, Calif.
San Bernardino	P. O. Box 112, Federal Building, San Bernardino, Calif.
Sequoia	Porterville, Calif.
Shasta-Trinity	1615 Continental Street, Redding, Calif.
Sierra	3525 E. Tulare Street, Fresno, Calif.
Six Rivers	331 J Street, Eureka, Calif.
Stanislaus	Sonora, Calif.
Tahoe	Nevada City, Calif.

APPROPRIATION OF WATER FOR MINING USE

The right to appropriate water for mining use has been established since the earliest days in California history (see *Hill* v. *King,* 1857, 8 Cal. 366). In fact, the California law of appropriation of water, as applied generally, has its origin in the customs of the early day miners who recognized among themselves rights based upon priority in time to divert water of natural streams upon the public domain for use on both riparian and distant lands, to the extent reasonably necessary for mining purposes (1 Wiel, Water Rights in the Western States (3d ed. 1911), 66 *et seq.*).

As the first placer mining claims became exhausted, the question arose whether a right to appropriate water could be changed from one claim to another and whether water formerly used for mining could be used for irrigation and other beneficial purposes under the original claim of right without loss of priority. It was judicially determined that changes in both place of use and point of diversion, as well as in purpose of use, could be made so long as other lawful users of water were not injured thereby (*Davis* v. *Gale,* 1867, 32 Cal. 26). In accordance with the existing statute, such changes under appropriations initiated by applications pursuant to the Water Commission Act or the Water Code can only be made by permission of the State Water Rights Board, after a finding that rights of others will not be impaired by the proposed change (Water Code Sections 1700-1705). Procedure necessary to secure such permission is set forth in Sections 738-742 of the Rules and Regulations of the State Water Rights Board (Cal. Adm. Code, Title 23, Waters).

It has never been questioned that water may properly be used for mining upon riparian land under claim of riparian right. Under California law, riparian rights do not attach to lands held by the Government until such lands have been transmitted to private ownership (*McKinley Bros.* v. *MacCauley,* 215 Cal. 229, 9 P. 2d 298; *Rindge* v. *Crags Land Co.,* 56 Cal. App. 247, 205 P. 36). However, it has been said that upon posting and filing of notice of location, a placer mining claim is for the time being no longer part of the public domain of the United States, and the claim, when patented, carries the title, by relation, back to the date of posting and filing (*Frey* v. *Garibaldi,* 23 Cal. App. 2d 83, 72 P. 2d 554).

Early decisions of the California courts are to the effect that both a valid mining location and entry under the homestead or pre-emption laws constitute the occupant a riparian owner (see *Crandall* v. *Woods,* 8 Cal. 136; *McGuire* v. *Brown,* 106 Cal. 660, 39 P. 1060; *Conkling* v. *Pacific Imp. Co.,* 87 Cal. 296, 25 P. 399; *Dripps* v. *Allison's Mines Co.,* 45 Cal. App. 95, 187 P. 448). In the *Crandall* case it was held that water flowing through a mining location cannot be appropriated later to the injury of the riparian rights of the owner of the mining claim, though the claim be unpatented. In *McGuire* v. *Brown* supra, the court quotes from *Sturr* v. *Beck,* 133 U.S. 547, 10 Sup. Ct. 350 as follows:

"When, however, the government ceases to be the sole proprietor, the right of the riparian owner attaches, and cannot be subsequently invaded."

Mining use, as defined by Section 665 of the Rules and Regulations of the State Water Rights Board, "includes any use wherein the water is applied to mining processes as for hydraulicking, for drilling and on concentrator tables, but not in connection with air blasts, compressors, etc."

If the miner finds it necessary to file an application to appropriate water for mining purposes (and this will be necessary if the claim has no riparian rights) it is best that he apply to the State Water Rights Board, 1401 21st Street, Sacramento, for a copy of the latest rules and regulations together with the proper forms for use with the application. No attempt is made herein to outline those rules nor the procedure as it would confuse rather than instruct the miner. One must have the rules and regulations as well as the necessary forms to reach understanding.

NO ASSISTANCE RENDERED IN SECURING RIGHT OF ACCESS TO POINT OF DIVERSION OR RIGHT OF WAY

The Board can be of no assistance in the matter of securing right of access to the stream or other source of supply or rights of way for ditches and conduit lines. In accepting an application or in issuing a permit, the Board does not affirm that applicant or permittee has right of access to the source of supply or necessary rights of way. While the Board will accept an application for filing before right of access has been secured, it will refuse to approve the application when it appears the applicant will be unable to secure such right.

It is worthy of note that all patents issued by the United States Land Office on homestead entries, enlarged homestead entries and stock raising entries are issued "subject to any vested and accrued water rights for mining, agricultural, manufacturing, or other purposes, and rights to ditches and reservoirs used in connection with such water rights as may be recognized and acknowledged by the local customs, laws, and decisions of courts."

SUPERVISION OVER DAMS

Division 3 of the Water Code, as amended, requires that construction or enlargement of any dam 25 feet or more in height from the level of the natural stream bed to crest of spillway provided it stores or may store more than 15 acre-feet of water, and any dam which stores or may store 50 acre-feet or more of water, provided it is more than six feet in height from the level of the natural stream bed to crest of spillway when completed, shall not be commenced without having first obtained written approval of the plans and specifications from the Department of Water Resources. Copies of this code and rules and regulations thereunder may be obtained upon request to the Department of Water Resources, 1120 N Street, Sacramento.

WATER POLLUTION

CONTENTS

WATER-POLLUTION CONTROL BOARDS

One of the major problems in some mining operations is the disposal of waste waters containing silt, tailings, and in some cases, directly toxic substances, such as cyanides. In California there are a number of agencies which are concerned with water pollution resulting from mining operations. These agencies include the State and County Health Departments, the State Department of Fish and Game, and the State and Regional Water Pollution Control Boards.

The 1949 Water Pollution Control Law states that persons proposing to discharge waste must first file a report of such discharge with the appropriate Regional Water Pollution Control Board. There are nine of these boards in the state, one for each of the major watershed areas, as shown on the accompanying map. These boards have the duty of coordinating the activities of all agencies interested in water pollution control and after reviewing the report of proposed waste discharge, the boards issue a set of requirements which govern the discharge. The powers and jurisdiction of the Pollution Control Boards are outlined in Division Seven of the Water Code. Any request for further information on water pollution problems may be directed to the agency concerned or to the appropriate Regional Water Pollution Control Boards, whose addresses are given on the accompanying list. The address of the State Water Pollution Control Board, which serves as an appellate board, is Room 316, 1227 O Street, Sacramento 14, California.

The California statutes define pollution as follows:

" 'Pollution' means an impairment of the quality of the waters of the State by sewage or industrial waste to a degree which does not create an actual hazard to the public health but which does adversely and unreasonably affect such waters for domestic, industrial, agricultural, navigational, recreational or other beneficial use, or which does adversely and unreasonably affect the ocean waters and bays of the State devoted to public recreation."

Responsibility for control of pollution is vested primarily in nine regional boards, one for each major watershed in the State, as shown on the accompanying map. The State Water Pollution Control Board is advisory to the regional boards and may review their actions. The following is a list of the addresses of the state and regional boards:

STATE WATER POLLUTION CONTROL BOARD
Room 316, 1227 O Street, Sacramento 14

NORTH COASTAL REGIONAL WATER POLLUTION CONTROL BOARD (No. 1)
1739 Fourth Street, Santa Rosa

SAN FRANCISCO BAY REGIONAL WATER POLLUTION CONTROL BOARD (No. 2)
1111 Jackson, Oakland 12

CENTRAL COASTAL REGIONAL WATER POLLUTION CONTROL BOARD (No. 3)
1108 Garden Street, San Luis Obispo

LOS ANGELES REGIONAL WATER POLLUTION CONTROL BOARD (No. 4)
217 W. First Street, Los Angeles 12

CENTRAL VALLEY REGIONAL WATER POLLUTION CONTROL BOARD (No. 5)
1232 F Street, Sacramento 14

LAHONTAN REGIONAL WATER POLLUTION CONTROL BOARD (No. 6)
407 West Line Street, Bishop

COLORADO RIVER BASIN REGIONAL WATER POLLUTION CONTROL BOARD (No. 7)
82-380 Miles Avenue, Indio

SANTA ANA REGIONAL WATER POLLUTION CONTROL BOARD (No. 8)
3691 Main Street, Riverside

SAN DIEGO REGIONAL WATER POLLUTION CONTROL BOARD (No. 9)
3441 University Avenue, San Diego 4

The regional boards regulate sewage and industrial wastes by the issuance and enforcement of waste discharge requirements. All new dischargers *must* file a report of their proposed discharge with the appropriate regional board. This is also true in the case of an existing discharger if there is any material change in the character, location or volume of the discharge. In addition, the boards may require any existing discharger to file a report upon request. They also may require waste dischargers to furnish such technical reports as the boards may specify. Persons failing to file reports of waste discharge or technical reports, upon request of a pollution control board, are guilty of a misdemeanor. Waste dischargers in violation of prescribed requirements are subject to cease and desist orders.

The powers and duties of the pollution control boards are outlined in Division 7 of the California Water Code. Requests for additional information may be addressed to the State Board or to the appropriate regional board.

In addition to the State and Regional Water Pollution Control Boards, it is well to make inquiry at the County Clerk's Office of the County wherein you propose to carry on mining and learn what County ordinances affecting your mining operations are in effect whether under Pollution, Health, or other Departmental names. Also refer to the sections of the Public Resources Code that regulate placer mining water pollution, pages 73-74.

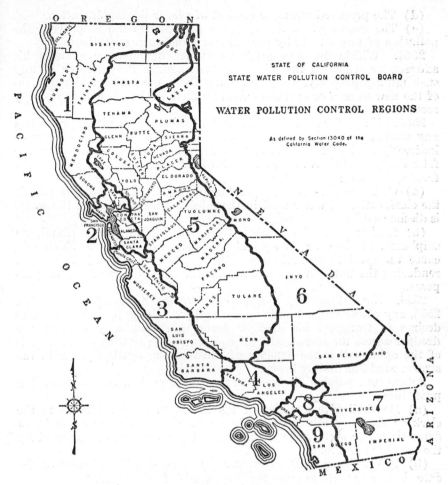

PLACER MINING WATER POLLUTION
Public Resources Code, Ch. 6.5 (Added by Stats. 1953 ch. 137)

2551. This chapter does not apply to any placer mine operator who holds a permit to operate from the California Debris Commission.*

2552. Any person, firm, or corporation who engages in the operation of a placer mine on any stream or on the watershed of any stream tributary directly or indirectly to the Sacramento or San Joaquin rivers shall record a verified statement in the office of the county recorder of the county in which his mine is situated, within 30 days after the commencement of operations.

2553. The verified statement shall be verified by the operator or by some one in his behalf and shall contain the following information:

(a) A description of the ground proposed to be mined by placer mining methods, described by United States Government subdivisions where possible.

(b) The names and addresses of the owners of the ground.

(c) The names and addresses of the operators of the mine.

---
* See pages 47-48 for discussion of Debris Commission Act.

(d) The proposed means or method of placer mining operation.

(e) The means which the operator proposes to use to prevent the pollution of any stream by the effluent from such operations.

2554. Within 10 days after an owner or operator changes his address, or transfers the ownership or changes the operator of any such mining property, a notice setting forth the names and addresses of the new owners or operators shall be filed in the office of the county recorder.

2555. No placer mining operator shall mine by the placer process on any stream or on the watershed of any stream tributary directly or indirectly to the Sacramento or San Joaquin rivers without taking the following precautions to prevent pollution of the stream by the effluent from operations:

(a) Constructing a settling pond or ponds of sufficient size to permit the clarification of water used in the mining processes before the water is discharged into the stream.

(b) Mixing with the effluent from mining operations aluminum sulphate and lime, or an equivalent clarifying substance which will cause the solid material in the effluent to coagulate and thus avoid rendering the water in the stream unfit for domestic water supply purposes.

2556. Notwithstanding the provisions of subdivision (b) of Section 2555, any placer miner who is operating by dredging process * and who desires to transport his dredger across a stream may conduct the dredger across the stream without constructing a settling pond, if he is of the opinion that the expense of constructing settling ponds in the stream would be unduly heavy.

Before transporting his dredger, the operator shall use the following procedure:

(a) He shall give a notice of his intent to cross a stream to the clerk or the secretary of each city or district owning or operating a domestic water supply the clarity of which is likely to be affected by the crossing operation.

(b) The notice shall be given at least seven days in advance of the date that he expects to cross the stream with his dredger.

(c) Upon the expiration of the notice the operator may during the following 48 hours conduct his dredger across the stream even though some turbidity may be caused by the crossing operation.

(d) After crossing the stream, the operator shall comply with the provisions of subdivision (b) of Section 2555.

2557. Any person, firm, or corporation who violates this chapter is guilty of a misdemeanor.

2558. The operation of any placer mine on ground not covered by a permit to the operator from the California Debris Commission, without compliance with the provisions of this chapter, is declared to be a public nuisance which may be enjoined upon suit brought by the district attorney of the county in which the operation has been conducted, or by any city or district whose domestic water supply is rendered unfit or dangerous for human consumption by the acts, or failure to act, of the operator. The superior court of the county in which the operation

---

* County dredging ordinances can be obtained from the appropriate county clerk. See Appendix I, page 110, for permit regulations regarding the operation of vacuum or suction dredges.

is conducted has jurisdiction to hear and determine the action and to award such relief as may be proper.

WATER USE AFFECTING FISH LIFE *

The manner in which water is used in mining operations must conform with certain provisions of the Fish and Game Code. On all rivers and streams in this State naturally frequented by fish the Fish and Game Commission and the Department of Fish and Game may require that any dam or other obstruction constructed thereon be provided with a suitable fishway to allow free passage for fish over or around such dam. In addition, flumes must be screened where necessary to prevent the loss of small, downstream-migrating fishes. Another general provision states that sufficient water must be released below any diversion to maintain fish life in the stream.

Further information on these or other matters pertaining to fish and game may be secured from local Department of Fish and Game personnel or by writing to the State Department of Fish and Game, Room 5099, 722 Capitol Ave., Sacramento.

Pertinent sections of the Fish and Game Code are reprinted below:

5500.   It is unlawful to use explosives in the waters of this State inhabited by fish, except under the terms of a permit first obtained by the user from the commission, or except in case of emergency, to remove an accidental obstruction to the flow of water.

5650.   It is unlawful to deposit in, permit to pass into, or place where it can pass into the waters of this State any of the following:

(a) Any petroleum, acid, coal or oil tar, lampblack, aniline, asphalt, bitumen, or residuary product of petroleum, or carbonaceous material or substance.

(b) Any refuse, liquid or solid, from any refinery, gas house, tannery, distillery, chemical works, mill or factory of any kind.

(c) Any sawdust, shavings, slabs, edgings.

(d) Any factory refuse, lime, or slag.

(e) Any cocculus indicus.

(f) Any substance or material deleterious to fish, plant life, or bird life.

5651.   Whenever it is determined by the department that a continuing and chronic condition of pollution exists, the department shall report such condition to the appropriate regional water pollution control board, and shall cooperate with and act through such board in obtaining correction in accordance with any laws administered by such board for control of practices for sewage and industrial waste disposal.

5800.   (a) It is unlawful to conduct any mining operations in the Trinity and Klamath River Fish and Game District between July 1st and November 30th, except when the debris, substances, tailings or other effluent from such operations do not and cannot pass into the waters in that district.

(b) It is unlawful between July 1st and November 30th, to pollute, muddy, contaminate, or roil the waters of the Trinity and Klamath River Fish and Game District. It is unlawful between those dates to deposit in or cause, suffer, or procure to be deposited in, permit to pass into or place where it can pass into such waters, any debris, substance

---

* The 1961 session of the State Legislature added Sections to the Fish and Game Code that regulate sand and gravel mining operations on specified rivers and the operation of vacuum or suction dredges. See Appendix I, page 110.

or tailings from hydraulic, placer, milling or other mining operation affecting the clarity of such waters. The clarity of such waters shall be deemed affected when such waters at a point a distance of one mile below the confluence of the Klamath River and the Salmon River or at a point a distance of one mile below the confluence of the South Fork of the Trinity River and the Trinity River contain fifty (50) parts per million, by weight, of suspended matter, not including vegetable matter in suspension and suspended matter occurring in the stream or streams due to an act of God.

(c) It is unlawful, between July 1st and November 30th, to carry on or operate any hydraulic mine of any kind on, along, or in any waters flowing into the Trinity and Klamath River District. However, nothing herein contained shall prevent the operation of a hydraulic mine where the tailings, substance, or debris, or other effluent therefrom does not or will not pass into the waters of the Trinity and Klamath River Fish and Game District, between such dates, and any person, firm or corporation engaged in hydraulic mining shall have the right until the fifteenth day of July to use water for the purpose of cleaning up.

(d) Any structure or contrivance which causes or contributes, in whole or in part, to the condition, the causing of which is in this section prohibited, is a public nuisance, and any person, firm or corporation maintaining or permitting it is guilty of maintaining a public nuisance, and it is the duty of the district attorney of the county where the condition occurs or the acts creating the public nuisance occur, to bring action to abate such nuisance.

5801.   Section 5800 does not affect any other laws applying to the territory included in the Trinity and Klamath River Fish and Game District which relate to birds, mammals, and fish.

5802.   Section 5800 does not apply to the construction, repair, or maintenance of public works by the Federal or State Government, or any political subdivision thereof.

5948.   No person shall cause or having caused, permit to exist any log jam or debris accumulation or any other artificial barrier, except a dam for the storage or diversion of water, public bridges and approaches thereto, groins, jetties, seawalls, breakwaters, bulkheads, wharves and piers permitted by law, and debris from mining operations, in any stream in this State, which will prevent the passing of fish up and down stream or which is deleterious to fish as determined by the commission, subject to review by the courts.

(Amended by Stats. 1957, Ch. 2039.)

12000.   The violation of any provision of this code, other than Section 12001, or of any rule, regulation, or order made or adopted under this code, is a misdemeanor.

(Minimum penalty for violating Sections 5651, 5800, and 5948 is $25.00 or 10 days; for paragraphs 5500 and 5650, $100.00 or 25 days.)

12015.   In addition to any other penalty provided, anyone convicted of unlawfully polluting, contaminating, or obstructing waters to the detriment of fish life in such waters, shall either be required to remove any substance placed in the waters, which can be removed, that caused the prohibited condition or to pay the costs of such removal by the department.

(Added by Stats. 1957, Ch. 2039.)

SAFETY REGULATIONS

CONTENTS

DIVISION OF INDUSTRIAL SAFETY

State safety regulations and codes are enforced by the State Division of Industrial Safety. All mining operations, where one or more persons are employed, are obligated to comply with the applicable safety orders of this Division. Although underground mining, quarrying, and gold dredging are covered by specific safety orders, many of the other safety orders are applicable in part to the mineral industry. Questions concerning this subject should be directed to the Division of Industrial Safety at either of the following addresses:

State Division of Industrial Safety
  State Building Annex
    455 Golden Gate Avenue
      San Francisco 2, California (Headquarters Office)
          and
State Division of Industrial Safety
  Room 5027, Los Angeles State Office Building
    107 South Broadway
      Los Angeles 12, California

List of Safety Orders

The list of Safety Rules and Safety Orders issued by the Division of Industrial Safety is printed below. These Safety Orders are for sale by the Printing Division, Documents Section, N. Seventh St. and Richards Blvd., Sacramento 14, California. A price list may be obtained from the Printing Division.

* Air pressure tank safety orders
  Boiler safety orders
  Compressed air safety orders governing work in compressed air
* Construction safety orders
* Electrical safety orders
  Elevator safety orders
* General industry safety orders
  Lamp parallel and scaffold safety orders
* Liquefied petroleum gases safety orders
  Logging and sawmill safety orders
* Mine safety orders
  Painting safety orders
  Petroleum safety orders, drilling and production
  Petroleum safety orders, refining, transportation and handling
* Pneumatic explosives loading safety orders
* Quarry and open pit mine safety orders
* Safety rules for gold dredges
  Ship and boat building safety orders
  Trench construction safety orders
  Tunnel safety orders
  Window cleaning safety orders

---

* Safety orders most used at mines and quarries.

ABANDONED EXCAVATIONS
(Health and Safety Code—Division 20, Ch. 4)

Sec. 24400   Every person owning land in fee simple or in possession thereof under lease or contract of sale who knowingly permits the existence on the premises of any abandoned mining shaft, pit, well, septic tank, cesspool or other abandoned excavation dangerous to persons legally on the premises or to minors under the age of twelve years, who fails to cover, or fence securely any such dangerous abandoned excavation and keep it so protected is guilty of a misdemeanor.

Sec. 24401   The board of supervisors may order securely covered or fenced abandoned mining excavations on unoccupied public lands in the county.

Sec. 24402   The board of supervisors shall order securely fenced or covered any abandoned mining shaft, pit, or other excavation on unoccupied land in the county wherever it appears to them, by proof submitted, that the excavation is dangerous or unsafe to man or beast. The cost of covering or fencing is a county charge.

Sec. 24403   Every person who maliciously removes or destroys any covering or fencing placed around any shaft, pit, or other excavation, as provided in this article, is guilty of a misdemeanor.

Mine Safety Orders, 1958, issued by the Division of Industrial Safety (see page 77) under the authority of the Labor Code, also refer to abandoned excavations:

Sec. 5954 (a) Every dangerous surface excavation in which work has been discontinued, including any tunnel, mine shaft, pit, well, septic tank, cesspool, or other abandoned excavation, shall be securely covered over, fenced, or otherwise effectively guarded.

TRANSPORTATION OF EXPLOSIVES

The California Vehicle Code, Division 11d, Transportation of Explosives (added by Stats. 1957, Ch. 1997) governs ". . . the operation of any motor vehicle on any public highway for the purpose of transporting any explosive in any amount when such transportation is rendered as a delivery service or for hire, or in any other event for the purpose of transporting any explosive in an amount in excess of 1,000 pounds." Included in the term "explosives" are "high explosives, black powder (low explosives), initiating or priming explosives, blasting caps, etc."

When the transportation of explosives is governed by the code, such explosives shall be transported over approved routes as designated and published in regulations of the State Fire Marshal, 1025 P Street, Sacramento 14. Such designated routes are required by this code and by the California Administrative Code (Section 1500, Article 1, Subchapter 10, Chapter 1, Title 19).

The Vehicle Code cited above also requires that a permit for such transportation be obtained from the California Department of Highway Patrol.

Failure to comply with these permit requirements or failure to transport explosives over approved routes as required by this code, except as otherwise permitted, is a misdemeanor.

The transportation of explosives, when not governed by the Vehicle Code as cited above, and the purchase of explosives are governed by the Health and Safety Code, Division 11, Sec. 12,000 et seq. as amended. This code requires that permits to receive explosives be issued by the "chief having the responsibility for the prevention and suppression of fire in the area in which the explosives are to be used." The State Fire Marshal prescribes the form to be used in making application for such permits. This code also requires that records be kept of all transactions involving the sales of explosives.

The code states in Section:

12113   Vehicles transporting explosives governed by the provisions of this part shall have displayed thereon or attached thereto such signs as are required by Section 599 of the Vehicle Code (Added by Stats. 1959 Ch. 1740, p. 19).

The Vehicle Code, Section 599, requires that on motor vehicles transporting explosives ". . . there shall be displayed upon each side and the rear of the exterior of such vehicle a sign upon which shall appear the word 'explosives,'. . . in letters not less than three inches in height upon a background of sharply contrasting color."

CORPORATE SECURITIES LAW OF CALIFORNIA

Promoters of mining enterprises through corporate form of organization are required under the Corporate Securities Law to obtain a permit from the Corporation Commissioner before collecting any consideration on preincorporation subscriptions for stock of a proposed California corporation or from California residents for stock of a foreign corporation. After incorporation, any subscription for stock of a domestic or foreign corporation can be taken only after a permit is first applied for and issued.

Solicitation of the public to become general or limited partners or joint venturers with the mining promoter requires that a permit first be obtained. Soliciting borrowed working capital from the public on promissory notes, debentures, bonds or other evidences of indebtedness, beneficial interests or profit sharing agreements, likewise require a permit. Warning also is given against sale of personally owned stock to directly or indirectly finance a mining corporation as this practice is prohibited by the Corporate Securities Law. Engaging in whole or in part in the business of reselling personally owned stock to the public constitutes such seller to be a broker requiring a securities broker's certificate.

Further information can be obtained from the offices of the State Division of Corporations: Room 401, 1020 N Street, Sacramento; Room 8117, Los Angeles State Office Building, 107 South Broadway, Los Angeles 12; and Room 7220, State Building, 350 McAllister Street, San Francisco 2.

ORE-BUYERS LICENSES

It is unlawful for any person to engage in the business of milling, sampling, concentrating, reducing, refining, purchasing, or receiving for sale, ores, concentrates, or amalgams bearing gold or silver, gold dust, gold or silver bullion, nuggets, or specimens without first procuring a license as provided by the Public Resources Code, Division 2, Chapter 3 and amendments thereto. A license is not required for any mill, sampler, concentrating or reduction plant used exclusively by the owner in sampling, milling, or reducing or concentrating ores produced by such owner.

Two kinds of ore-buyers' licenses are issued: (1) *Limited*, limiting the buyers to $1,000 in purchases for the calendar year; (2) *Unlimited*, carrying no limit on purchases during the calendar year. Application forms for and further information about licenses may be procured from the State Division of Mines and Geology, Ferry Building, San Francisco 11, California.

ORE-BUYERS LICENSE ACT, COMMONLY REFERRED TO AS "THE HIGH GRADE BILL"

Public Resources Code, Division 2, Mines and Mining, Chapter 3. Regulating and Licensing Purchasers of Gold or Silver Ores, Concentrates, or Amalgams. (Chapter 93, Statutes of 1939.)

2250. It is unlawful for any person to engage in the business of milling, sampling, concentrating, reducing, refining, purchasing, or receiving for sale, ores, concentrates or amalgams bearing gold or silver, gold dust, gold or silver bullion, nuggets, or specimens without first procuring the license provided for by this chapter.

2251. Every person who annually mills, samples, concentrates, reduces, refines, purchases, or receives for sale such ores, concentrates, or amalgams of the total value of one thousand dollars or more, shall pay a license tax of fifteen dollars a year to the State. Every person who annually mills, samples, concentrates, reduces, refines, purchases, or receives for sale such ores, concentrates, or amalgams, of the total value of less than one thousand dollars shall pay a license tax of two dollars a year to the State.

2252. No license shall be granted to any person, firm, or association unless such person and the members of such firm and association are bona fide residents of the State, and of good moral character. No license shall be granted to any joint stock company or corporation unless such company or corporation is duly qualified to exist and do business under the laws of this State or unless such company or corporation has complied with all the laws of this State authorizing foreign corporations to do business in this State.

This chapter shall not be construed as requiring a license for any mill, sampler, concentration or reduction plant used exclusively by the owner in sampling, milling, or reducing or concentrating ores produced by such owner.

2253. The application for a license to carry on such business shall be made to the State Geologist, and shall contain the full names and addresses of the applicants, if natural persons, and in the case of firms and associations the full names and addresses of the members thereof, and in the case of corporations, the full names and addresses of the officers and directors thereof, and the place or places where the business is to be carried on. The application shall be sworn to by the person making it.

2254. Every license granted shall date from the first day of the month in which it is issued and expire on the thirty-first day of the following December. The license or copies thereof shall be kept conspicuously displayed in the place or places of business of the licensee within the State.

2255. Every application shall be filed not less than thirty days prior to the granting of the license. Notice of the filing of the application shall be posted in the office of the State Geologist and shall be published, at the cost of the applicant, once a week for three successive weeks in a newspaper published in the county or counties where the business is to be carried on.

2256. Protest may be made by any person to the issuing of a license, and when such protests are filed with the State Geologist, he shall give notice of and hold a public hearing upon the protest before issuing the license. The State Geologist may reject any application for a license after a hearing upon the protest. The proceedings shall be conducted in accordance with Chapter 5 of Part 1 of Division 3 of Title 2 of the Government Code, and the State Geologist shall have all the powers granted therein. (Amended by Stats. 1945, Ch. 879.)

2257. The State Geologist may revoke any license for failure on the part of the licensee to observe any of the provisions of this chapter, or when the licensee has violated the provisions of any law of the State relating to ore buying or of any law relating to larceny or receiving stolen property. The proceedings shall be conducted in accordance with Chapter 5 of Part 1 of Division 3 of Title 2 of the Government Code, and the State Geologist shall have all the powers granted therein. (Amended by Stats. 1945, Ch. 879.)

2258. A daily calendar shall be kept of all hearings by the State Geologist, which shall be posted in a conspicuous place in his office for at least three days before the date of such hearing. The State Geologist shall keep a record of all charges, protests, and hearings, and may refuse to issue and shall suspend or revoke any license for any good cause shown, within the meaning and purpose of this chapter. (Amended by Stats. 1945, Ch. 879.)

2259. When it is shown that any licensee or applicant, either before or after conviction, is guilty of any conduct in violation of this or any law relating to such business, the State Geologist shall suspend or revoke the license of the licensee, or reject the application of the applicant. (Amended by Stats. 1945, Ch. 879.)

2260. Whenever, for any reason, a license is revoked, the State Geologist shall not issue another license to the licensee until the expiration of at least one year from the date of revocation of the license. (Amended by Stats. 1945, Ch. 879.)

2261.   (Repealed by Stats. 1945, Ch. 879.)
2262.   (Repealed by Stats. 1945, Ch. 879.)
2263.   (Repealed by Stats. 1945, Ch. 879.)
2264.   For the making of the transcript the State Geologist shall collect from the person ordering it, twenty-five cents per folio of one hundred words, and twenty-five cents for certifying it.

2265.   Every person engaged in a business licensed under this chapter shall keep and preserve a book in which shall be entered at the time of the delivery of any ores, concentrates or amalgams bearing gold or silver, gold dust, gold or silver bullion, nuggets, or specimens:

(a)   The name of the person on whose behalf such ores, concentrates, gold dust, gold or silver bullion, nuggets or specimens are delivered.

(b)   The weight, or amount, and a short description of each lot thereof.

(c)   The name and location of the mine or claim from which it is stated that the lot has been mined or procured.

(d)   The name of the person delivering it.

(e)   The date of delivery.

(f)   Whether the person making the delivery is a lessee, superintendent, foreman, or workman in such mine.

2266.   Such book shall be open for inspection by the State Geologist, his deputies, officers, and agents, on every day except Sundays and legal holidays, between the hours of nine o'clock a.m. and five o'clock p.m.

If any person, on his own behalf or being duly authorized by another, makes and files an affidavit with the State Geologist, stating that, to his best knowledge and belief, he or his principals, as the case may be, has, within the three months next preceding the filing of the affidavit, sustained a loss of any of the property described in Section 2265, by theft or trespass, and that he believes that such property was delivered to a licensee under this chapter, naming the licensee, the State Geologist shall forthwith issue a permit to such person to examine the book kept by such licensee as provided in this chapter. Upon the presentation of the permit to the licensee, such person may inspect and examine the entries made in such book during said period of three months, on the same terms and conditions as the State Geologist.

2267.   Every licensee under this chapter shall file monthly with the State Geologist a report of all purchases made under this chapter. The reports shall be made upon forms prescribed by the State Geologist and shall contain the information required by this chapter. Any licensee who fails or refuses to comply with the provisions of this section is guilty of a misdemeanor.

2268.   All officers and employees empowered by law or authorized by a superior to enforce the provisions of this chapter are vested with the powers of peace officers to enforce the provisions hereof and may seize and hold any ores, concentrates, or amalgams bearing gold or silver, gold dust, gold or silver bullion, nuggets, or specimens wherever found and whenever there appear to be reasonable grounds to believe such property has been stolen or otherwise illegally taken, and may hold such property for use as evidence in any action which may be brought.

2269.   Whenever any property so seized and held appears to be no longer of use as evidence, it shall be delivered to the owner thereof upon proof of such ownership. Any person claiming ownership may file a petition in the superior court of the county of his residence showing his claim or right thereto. A copy of the petition shall be served, at least twenty days before the hearing thereof, upon the Attorney General, who shall answer the petition. Upon the hearing of the petition, the court shall try the issue as issues are tried in civil actions, and if it determines that the petitioner is entitled to the property, the court shall order it delivered to the petitioner.

2270. If the ores, concentrates or amalgams are not so delivered to the owner thereof, they shall, after a period of five years from the date upon which they were seized and held, escheat to the State upon action brought by the Attorney General in the superior court in and for the county of Sacramento. All persons claiming to be owner or having any right or interest therein shall be joined as parties defendant in the action. Service of process shall be made as summons is served in other civil actions upon any known claimant and by publication thereof, before the trial of the action, at least once a week for three successive weeks in a newspaper of general circulation printed and published in the county of Sacramento.

2271. Upon the trial, the court shall hear all parties who have appeared. If any party proves ownership or that he has any right or interest therein, the court shall make an order for the delivery of the property to him, or the sale thereof and a distribution of the proceeds to discharge the right or interest which he has therein, the balance of the proceeds to escheat to the State; otherwise, the court shall declare the property to have escheated to the State. Thereafter the State Geologist may sell the ores, concentrates and amalgams not theretofore sold by court order and shall account for and report the proceeds of the sale to the State Controller and at the same time remit the money to the State Treasury to be credited to the General Fund. (Amended by Stats. 1943, Ch. 211.)

2272. Any licensee under this chapter who fails or neglects or refuses to keep and preserve the book herein provided for, shall forfeit his license and shall also be liable to the penalties provided in Section 2274.

Any licensee or other person who knowingly makes any false entries upon such book, or knowingly enters or causes to be entered any false or fictitious names upon such book, shall be liable to the penalties provided in Section 2274.

Any licensee who refuses to permit any duly authorized person to inspect such book or the entries therein shall forfeit his license and is guilty of a misdemeanor.

2273. Any person who knowingly makes any false statements concerning any of the facts required to be stated in Sections 2265 or 2266 is guilty of a misdemeanor.

2274. Any violation of Sections 2250, 2251, 2252, 2265, 2266, 2267, or 2272 is a misdemeanor punishable by a fine of not less than one hundred dollars and not more than one thousand dollars, or by imprisonment in the county jail for not less than thirty days nor more than six months, or both such fine and imprisonment. The State Geologist shall notify the district attorney of the county in which the offense occurs of any such violation, and the district attorney shall institute criminal proceedings for the enforcement of this chapter before any court of competent jurisdiction.

All forfeited bail and fines received by any court under the provisions of this section shall as soon as practicable after the receipt thereof be deposited with the county treasurer of the county in which such court is situated. Amounts so deposited shall be paid at least once a month as follows: 50 percent to the State Treasurer by warrant of the county auditor drawn upon the requisition of the clerk or judge of said court, to be deposited in the State treasury to the credit of the General Fund on order of the State Controller; and 50 percent to the city treasurer of the city, if incorporated, or to the county treasurer of the county in which the prosecution is conducted. (Amended by Stats. 1943, Ch. 211 and Stats. 1953, Ch. 523.)

2275.   All money received by the State Geologist under this chapter, shall be accounted for and reported monthly to the State Controller, to be remitted by the Controller to the State Treasury to the credit of the General Fund. All money deposited with the State Geologist for fees for licenses which have not been granted shall be retained by him in the trust fund of the division to be remitted to the State Treasurer upon the issuance of the license or returned to the applicant in case a license is refused. (Added by Stats. 1939, Ch. 97, as part of codification; amended by Stats. 1943, Ch. 211.)

FEDERAL GOLD REGULATIONS

Under provisions of the Gold Reserve Act of 1934, approved January 30, 1934 (48 Stat. 337; 31 U.S.C. 440) the Director of the Mint may issue or cause to be issued licenses or other authorizations permitting the acquisition and holding, transportation, melting and treating, importing and exporting of gold which the Director is satisfied is required for legitimate and customary use in industry, profession, or art, by persons regularly engaged in the business of furnishing or processing gold for industry, profession, or art, or for sale to the United States, or in an industry, profession, or art in which stocks of gold in excess of 50 fine troy ounces are required to be maintained by the applicant.

Gold in its natural state means gold recovered from natural sources and which has not been melted, smelted, or refined, or otherwise treated by heating or by a chemical or electrical process such gold may be acquired, transported within the United States, imported, or held in custody for domestic account without the necessity of holding a license therefor.

Gold amalgam which results from the addition of mercury to gold in its natural state, recovered from natural deposits in the United States or a place subject to the jurisdiction thereof, may be heated to a temperature sufficient to separate the mercury from the gold (but not to the melting temperature of the gold) without a license by the person who recovered the gold from such deposits, or his duly authorized agent or employee. The retort sponge so resulting may be held and transported by such person without a license; provided, however, that no such person may hold at any one time an amount of such retort sponge which exceeds 200 troy ounces in fine gold content. Such retort sponge may be acquired from such persons by the United States or by persons holding licenses on forms obtained from the Director of the Mint, Treasury Department, Washington, D.C.

Except as provided in the Gold Reserve Act in secs. 54.12 to 54.20 inclusive, and in secs. 54.32 and 54.33, gold in its natural state may be melted or treated or exported only to the extent permitted by, and subject to the conditions prescribed in, or pursuant to, secs. 54.21 to 54.27, inclusive.

Further information about and copies of Federal gold regulations may be obtained from the United States Mint at Duboce and Market Streets, San Francisco, California.

ANNOTATED BIBLIOGRAPHY

General references

Ricketts, A. H., 1943, American mining law: California Div. Mines Bull. 123, 1018 pp. (contains a wealth of data on mineral rights; out of print).

Robie, E. H. (Ed.), 1959, Economics of the mineral industries: Am. Inst. Min. Met. Eng., New York, 755 pp. (mineral titles and tenure, including foreign aspects, pp. 81-129).

Rocky Mountain Mineral Law Foundation, 1960, The American law of mining: Mathew Bender and Co., Inc., New York, 5 vols. (a modern, comprehensive, compiled treatise on mining law).

Rocky Mountain Mineral Law Foundation, 1955-1961, Rocky Mountain Mineral Law Institute proceedings, First annual (1955) through Sixth annual (1961): Mathew Bender and Co., Inc., New York, 1 vol. each Institute (articles published were the bases for lectures delivered during each annual Rocky Mountain Mineral Law Institute presented by the Foundation at the University of Colorado, Boulder, authors selected for their eminence in their respective fields).

Winchell, H. V., and Douglas, Archibald, 1941, Mining laws in Mining Engineers Handbook 3d ed. by Robert Peele and J. A. Church. J. Wiley and Sons, New York, sec. 24, pp. 1-40 (an excellent general reference on various aspects of mining law).

California references

Dana, S. T., and Krueger, Myron, 1958, California lands—ownership, use and management: The American Forestry Association, Washington, D.C., 308 pp. (though written because of forestry problems, has a relatively large amount of information on mining and petroleum. Contains a detailed annotated bibliography).

Saul, R. B., 1962, Mineral monuments: Mineral Information Service, in press. (Describes mineral monument system and survey; provides list of mineral monuments established in California.)

Weber, F. H., Jr., 1961, Mineral rights: Mineral Information Service, vol. 14, no. 2. (A comprehensive compilation of the problems facing an individual seeking to initiate mineral rights in California.)

Publications of the U.S. Department of Interior

U.S. Bureau of Land Management, various dates, various pamphlets containing parts of Title 43 of the Code of Federal Regulations. Title 43 contains regulations in regard to development of mineral resources on federal lands.

U.S. Bureau of Land Management, 1955, Lode and placer mining regulations: U.S. Bur. Land Management Circular 1941, 26 pp. (Part 185, Title 43, Code of Federal Regulations).

U.S. Bureau of Land Management, 1958, Multiple use of mining claims—some facts and guidelines for miners and mineral locators: U.S. Dept. of Interior, 13 pp. (pamphlet available from Government Printing Office, Washington, D.C., for 10¢).

U.S. Bureau of Land Management, 1960, Regulations for oil and gas leasing on federal public lands: U.S. Bureau of Land Management Circular 2037, 13 pp. (Part 192, Title 43, Code of Federal Regulations).

U.S. Department of the Interior, undated Leasing and operating regulations for the submerged lands of the outer continental shelf: U.S. Dept. Interior, 44 pp. (Part 250 (oil and gas) Title 30 and Part 20 (mineral deposits) Title 43, Code of Federal Regulations).

State legal guides

Gallagher, M. J., 1954, Nevada mining claim procedures: State of Nevada, 51 pp. (available from State Printing Office, Carson City).

Oregon Department of Mineral Industries, 1954, Mining Laws of the State of Oregon: Oregon Dept. Geol. and Min. Ind., 32 pp. (available from Oregon Department of Geology and Mineral Industries, Portland, for 50¢).

Verity, V. H., 1957, Laws and regulations governing mineral rights in Arizona: Arizona Dept. Min. Res., 80 pp. (available from the Arizona Department of Mineral Resources, Phoenix, for 30¢).

APPENDIX I AND II

APPENDIX I

CONTENTS

PUBLIC LAW 585

On August 12, 1954 the Multiple Mineral Development Law went into effect. This law is of particular concern to persons interested in uranium. In view of its importance, the bill has been reproduced below in its entirety. See discussion in guide, page 14.

Public Law 585 – 83d Congress
Chapter 730 – 2d Session
S. 3344

AN ACT

To amend the mineral leasing laws and the mining laws to provide for multiple mineral development of the same tracts of the public lands, and for other purposes.

Be it enacted by the Senate and House of Representatives of the United States of America in Congress assembled, That (a) subject to the conditions and provisions of this Act and to any valid intervening rights acquired under the laws of the United States, any mining claim located under the mining laws of the United States subsequent to July 31, 1939, and prior to February 10, 1954, on lands of the United States, which at the time of location were— *[Mineral leasing claims. Preference categories. 30 USCA 521]*

(1) included in a permit or lease issued under the mineral leasing laws; or

(2) covered by an application or offer for a permit or lease which had been filed under the mineral leasing laws; or

(3) known to be valuable for minerals subject to disposition under the mineral leasing laws,

shall be effective to the same extent in all respects as if such lands at the time of location, and at all times thereafter, had not been so included or covered or known: *Provided, however,* That, in order to be entitled to the benefits of this Act, the owner of any such mining claim located prior to January 1, 1953, must have posted and filed for record, within the time allowed by the provisions of the Act of August 12, 1953 (67 Stat. 539), an amended notice of location as to such mining claim, *[30 USC 501-504.]* stating that such notice was filed pursuant to the provisions of said Act of August 12, 1953, and for the purpose of obtaining the benefits thereof: *And provided further,* That in order to obtain the benefits of this Act, the owner of any such mining claim located subsequent to December 31, 1952, and prior to February 10, 1954, not later than one hundred and twenty days after the date of enactment of this Act, must post on such claim in the manner required for posting notice of location of mining claims and file for record in the office where the notice or certificate of location of such claim is of record an amended notice

(93)

of location for such claim, stating that such notice is filed pursuant to the provisions of this Act and for the purpose of obtaining the benefits thereof and, within said one hundred and twenty day period, if such owner shall have filed a uranium lease application as to the tract covered by such mining claim, must file with the Atomic Energy Commission a withdrawal of such uranium lease application or, if a uranium lease shall have issued pursuant thereto, a release of such lease, and must record a notice of the filing of such withdrawal or release in the county office wherein such notice or certificate of location shall have been filed for record.

Labor and improvements.

(b) Labor performed or improvements made after the original location of and upon or for the benefit of any mining claim which shall be entitled to the benefits of this Act under the provisions of subsection (a) of this section 1, shall be recognized as applicable to such mining claim for all purposes to the same extent as if the validity of such mining claim were in no respect dependent upon the provisions of this Act.

Withdrawal of lands, etc.

(c) As to any land covered by any mining claim which is entitled to the benefits of this Act under the provisions of subsection (a) of this section 1, any withdrawal or reservation of lands made after the original location of such mining claim is hereby modified and amended so that the effect thereof upon such mining claim shall be the same as if such mining claim had been located upon lands of the United States which, subsequent to July 31, 1939, and prior to the date of such withdrawal or reservation, were subject to location under the mining laws of the United States.

30 USCA 522

SEC. 2.   (a) If any mining claim which shall have been located subsequent to December 31, 1952, and prior to December 11, 1953, and which shall be entitled to the benefits of this Act, shall cover any lands embraced within any mining claim which shall have been located prior to January 1, 1953, and which shall be entitled to the benefits of this Act, then as to such area of conflict said mining claim so located subsequent to December 31, 1952, shall be deemed to have been located December 11, 1953.

(b) If any mining claim hereafter located shall cover any lands embraced within any mining claim which shall have been located prior to February 10, 1954, and which shall be entitled to the benefits of this Act, then as to such area of conflict said mining claim hereafter located shall be deemed to have been located one hundred and twenty-one days after the date of the enactment of this Act.

Uranium leases, etc. 30 USCA 523

SEC. 3.   (a) Subject to the conditions and provisions of this Act and to any valid prior rights acquired under the laws of the United States, the owner of any pending uranium lease application or of any uranium lease shall have, for a period of one hundred and twenty days after the date of enactment of this Act, as limited in subsection (b) of this section 3, the right to locate mining claims upon the lands covered by said application or lease.

(b) Any rights under any such mining claim so hereafter located pursuant to the provisions of subsection (a) of this section 3 shall be subject to any rights of the owner of any mining claim which was located prior to February 10, 1954, and which was valid at the date of the enactment of this Act or which may acquire validity under the provisions of this Act. As to any lands covered by a uranium lease and also by a pending uranium lease application, the right of mining location under this section 3, as between the owner of said lease and the owner of said application, shall be deemed as to such conflict area to be vested in the owner of said lease. As to any lands embraced in more than one such pending uranium lease application, such right of mining location, as between the owners of such conflicting applications, shall be deemed to be vested in the owner of the prior application. Priority of such an application shall be determined by the time of posting on a tract then available for such leasing of a notice of lease application in accordance with paragraph (c) of the Atomic Energy Commission's Domestic Uranium Program Circular 7 (10 C. F. R. 60.7 (c)) provided there shall have been timely compliance with the other provisions of said paragraph (c) or, if there shall not have been such timely compliance, then by the time of the filing of the uranium lease application with the Atomic Energy Commission. Any rights under any mining claim located under the provisions of this section 3 shall terminate at the expiration of thirty days after the filing for record of the notice or certificate of location of such mining claim unless, within said thirty-day period, the owner of the uranium lease application or uranium lease upon which the location of such mining claim was predicated shall have filed with the Atomic Energy Commission a withdrawal of said application or a release of said lease and shall have recorded a notice of the filing of such withdrawal or release in the county office wherein such notice or certificate of location shall be of record.

(c) Except as otherwise provided in subsections (a) and (b) of this section 3, no mining claim hereafter located shall be valid as to any lands which at the time of such location were covered by a uranium lease application or a uranium lease. Any tract upon which a notice of lease application has been posted in accordance with said paragraph (c) of said Circular 7 shall be deemed to have been included in a uranium lease application from and after the time of the posting of such notice of lease application: *Provided*, That there shall have been timely compliance with the other provisions of said paragraph (c) or, if there shall not have been such timely compliance, then from and after the time of the filing of a uranium lease application with the Atomic Energy Commission.

SEC. 4. Every mining claim or millsite— Future mining claims, etc. 30 U.S.C.A. 524

(1) heretofore located under the mining laws of the United States which shall be entitled to benefits under the first three sections of this Act; or

(2) located under the mining laws of the United States after the effective date of passage of this Act, shall be subject, prior to issuance of a patent therefor, to a reservation to the United States of all Leasing Act minerals and of the right (as limited in section 6 hereof) of the United States, its lessees, permittees, and licensees to enter upon the land covered by such mining claim or millsite and to prospect for, drill for, mine, treat, store, transport, and remove Leasing Act minerals and to use so much of the surface and subsurface of such mining claim or millsite as may be necessary for such purposes, and whenever reasonably necessary, for the purpose of prospecting for, drilling for, mining, treating, storing, transporting, and removing Leasing Act minerals on and from other lands; and any patent issued for any such mining claim or millsite shall contain such reservation as to, but only as to, such lands covered thereby which at the time of the issuance of such patent were— Mineral reservation to U. S.

(a) included in a permit or lease issued under the mineral leasing laws; or

(b) covered by an application or offer for a permit or lease filed under the mineral leasing laws; or

(c) known to be valuable for minerals subject to disposition under the mineral leasing laws.

SEC. 5. Subject to the conditions and provisions of this Act, mining claims and millsites may hereafter be located under the mining laws of the United States on lands of the United States which at the time of location are— Location. 30 U.S.C.A. 525

(a) included in a permit or lease issued under the mineral leasing laws; or

(b) covered by an application or offer for a permit or lease filed under the mineral leasing laws; or

(c) known to be valuable for minerals subject to disposition under the mineral leasing laws;

to the same extent in all respects as if such lands were not so included or covered or known.

SEC. 6. (a) Where the same lands are being utilized for mining operations and Leasing Act operations, each of such operations shall be conducted, so far as reasonably practicable, in a manner compatible with such multiple use. Mining and Leasing Act operations. 30 U.S.C.A. 526

(b) Any mining operations pursuant to rights under any unpatented or patented mining claim or millsite which shall be subject to a reservation to the United States of Leasing Act minerals as provided in this Act, shall be conducted, so far as reasonably practicable, in a manner which will avoid damage to any known deposit of any Leasing Act mineral. Subject to the provisions of subsection (d) of this section 6, mining operations shall be so conducted as not to endanger or materially interfere with any existing surface or underground improvements, workings, or facilities which may have been made for the purpose of Leasing Act operations, or with the utilization of such improvements, workings, or facilities.

(c) Any Leasing Act operations on lands covered by an unpatented or patented mining claim or millsite which shall be subject to a reservation to the United States of Leasing Act minerals as provided in this Act shall be conducted, so far as reasonably practicable, in a manner which will avoid damage to any known deposit of any mineral not so reserved from such mining claim or millsite. Subject to the provisions of subsection (d) of this section 6, Leasing Act operations shall be so conducted as not to endanger or materially interfere with any existing surface or underground improvements, workings, or facilities which may have been made for the purpose of mining operations, or with the utilization of such improvements, workings, or facilities.

(d) If, upon petition of either the mining operator or the Leasing Act operator, any court of competent jurisdiction shall find that a particular use in connection with one of such operations cannot be reasonably and properly conducted without endangering or materially interfering with the then existing improvements, workings, or facilities of the other of such operations or with the utilization thereof, and shall find that under the conditions and circumstances, as they then appear, the injury or damage which would result from denial of such particular use would outweigh the injury or damage which would result to such then existing improvements, workings, or facilities or from interference with the utilization thereof if that particular use were allowed, then and in such event such court may permit such use upon payment (or upon furnishing of security determined by the court to be adequate to secure payment) to the party or parties who would be thus injured or damaged, of an amount to be fixed by the court as constituting fair compensation for the then reasonably contemplated injury or damage which would result to such then existing improvements, workings, or facilities or from interference with the utilization thereof by reason of the allowance of such particular use.

(e) Where the same lands are being utilized for mining operations and Leasing Act operations, then upon request of the party conducting either of said operations, the party conducting the other of said operations shall furnish to and at the expense of such requesting party copies of any information which said other party may have, as to the situs of any improvements, workings, or facilities theretofore made upon such lands, and upon like request, shall permit such requesting party, at the risk of such requesting party, to have access at reasonable times to any such improvements, workings, or facilities for the purpose of surveying and checking or determining the situs thereof. If damage to or material interference with a party's improvements, workings, facilities, or with the utilization thereof shall result from such party's failure, after request, to so furnish to the requesting party such information or from denial of such access, such failure or denial shall relieve the requesting party of any liability for the damage or interference resulting by reason of such failure or denial. Failure of a party to furnish requested information or access shall not impose upon such party any liability to the requesting party other than for such costs of court and attorney's fees as may be allowed to the requesting party in enforcing by court action the obligations of this section as to the furnishing of information and access. The obligation hereunder of any party to furnish requested information shall be limited to map and survey information then available to such party with respect to the situs of improvements, workings, and facilities and the furnishing thereof shall not be deemed to constitute any representation as to the accuracy of such information.

SEC. 7. (a) Any applicant, offeror, permittee, or lessee under the mineral leasing laws may file in the office of the Secretary of the Interior, or in such office as the Secretary may designate, a request for publication of notice of such application, offer, permit, or lease, provided expressly, that not less than ninety days prior to the filing of such request for publication there shall have been filed for record in the county office of record for the county in which the lands covered thereby are situate a notice of the filing of such application or offer or of the issuance of such permit or lease which notice shall set forth the date of such filing or issuance, the name and address of the applicant, offeror, permittee or lessee and the description of the lands covered by such application, offer, permit or lease, showing the section or sections of the public land surveys which embrace the lands covered by such application, offer, permit, or lease, or if such lands are unsurveyed, either the section or sections which would probably embrace such lands when the public lands surveys are extended to such lands or a tie by courses and distances to an approved United States mineral monument.

Unpatented mining claims.

Procedure for determination.

Filing of notice.
30 U.S.C.A. 527

The filing of such request for publication shall be accompanied by a certified copy of such recorded notice and an affidavit or affidavits of a person or persons over twenty-one years of age setting forth that the affiant or affiants have examined the lands involved in a reasonable effort to ascertain whether any person or persons were in actual possession of or engaged in the working of such lands or any part thereof, and, if no person or persons were found to be in actual possession of or engaged in the working of said lands or any part thereof on the date of such examination, setting forth such fact, or, if any person or persons were so found to be in actual possession or engaged in such working on the date of such examination, setting forth the name and address of each such person, unless affiant shall have been unable through reasonable inquiry to obtain information as to the name and address of any such person, in which event the affidavit shall set forth fully the nature and results of such inquiry.

The filing of such request for publication shall also be accompanied by the certificate of a title or abstract company, or of a title abstractor, or of an attorney, based upon such company's, abstractor's, or attorney's examination of the instruments affecting the lands involved, of record in the public records of the county in which said lands are situate as shown by the indices of the public records in the county office of record for said county, setting forth the name of any person disclosed by said instruments to have an interest in said lands under any unpatented mining claim heretofore located, together with the address of such person if disclosed by such instruments of record.

Thereupon the Secretary of the Interior, or his designated representative, at the expense of the requesting person (who, prior to the commencement of publication, must furnish the agreement of the publisher to hold such requesting person alone responsible for charges of publication), shall cause notice of such application, offer, permit, or lease to be published in a newspaper having general circulation in the county in which the lands involved are situate.

Such notice shall describe the lands covered by such application, offer, permit, or lease, as provided heretofore in the notice to be filed in the office of record of the county in which the lands covered are situate, and shall notify whomever it may concern that if any person claiming or asserting under, or by virtue of, any unpatented mining claim heretofore located, any right or interest in Leasing Act minerals as to such lands or any part thereof, shall fail to file in the office where such request for publication was filed (which office shall be specified in such notice) and within one hundred fifty days from the date of the first publication of such notice (which date shall be specified in such notice), a verified statement which shall set forth, as to such unpatented mining claim:

(1) The date of location;
(2) The book and page of recordation of the notice or certificate of location;

4—64993

(3) The section or sections of the public land surveys which embrace such mining claim; or if such lands are unsurveyed, either the section or sections which would probably embrace such mining claim when the public land surveys are extended to such lands or a tie by courses and distances to an approved United States mineral monument;

(4) Whether such claimant is a locator or purchaser under such location; and

(5) The name and address of such claimant and names and addresses so far as known to the claimant of any other person or persons claiming any interest or interests in or under such unpatented mining claim;

such failure shall be conclusively deemed (i) to constitute a waiver and relinquishment by such mining claimant of any and all right, title, and interest under such mining claim as to, but only as to, Leasing Act minerals, and (ii) to constitute a consent by such mining claimant that such mining claim and any patent issued therefor, shall be subject to the reservation specified in section 4 of this Act, and (iii) to preclude thereafter any assertion by such mining claimant of any right or title to or interest in any Leasing Act mineral by reason of such mining claim.

If such notice is published in a daily paper, it shall be published in the Wednesday issue for nine consecutive weeks, or, if in a weekly paper, in nine consecutive issues, or, if in a semiweekly or triweekly paper, in the issue of the same day of each week for nine consecutive weeks.

Within fifteen days after the date of first publication of such notice, the person requesting such publication (1) shall cause a copy of such notice to be personally delivered to or to be mailed by registered mail addressed to each person in possession or engaged in the working of the land whose name and address is shown by an affidavit filed as aforesaid, and to each person who may have filed, as to any lands described in said notice, a request for notices, as provided in subsection (d) of this section 7, and shall cause a copy of such notice to be mailed by registered mail to each person whose name and address is set forth in the title or abstract company's or title abstractor's or attorney's certificate filed as aforesaid, as having an interest in the lands described in said notice under any unpatented mining claim hertofore located, such notice to be directed to such person's address as set forth in such certificate; and (2) shall file in the office where said request for publication was filed an affidavit showing that copies have been so delivered or mailed.

(b) If any claimant under any unpatented mining claim heretofore located which embraces any of the lands described in any notice published in accordance with the provisions of subsection (a) of this section 7 shall fail to file a verified statement, as above provided, within one hundred and fifty days from the date of the first publication of such notice, such failure shall be conclusively deemed, except as otherwise provided in subsection (e) of this section 7, (i) to constitute a waiver and relinquishment by such mining claimant of any and all right, title, and interest under such mining claim as to, but only as to, Leasing Act minerals, and (ii) to constitute a consent by such mining claimant that such mining claim and any patent issued therefor, shall be subject to the reservation specified in section 4 of this Act, and (iii) to preclude thereafter any assertion by such mining claimant of any right or title to or interest in any Leasing Act mineral by reason of such mining claim.

(c) If any verified statement shall be filed by a mining claimant as provided in subsection (a) of this section 7, then the Secretary of the Interior or his designated representative shall fix a time and place for a hearing to determine the validity and effectiveness of the mining claimant's asserted right or interest in Leasing Act minerals, which place of hearing shall be in the county where the lands in question or parts thereof are located, unless the mining claimant agrees otherwise. The procedures with respect to notice of such a hearing and the conduct thereof, and in respect to appeals, shall follow the then established general procedures and rules of practice of the Department of the Interior in respect to contests or protests affecting public lands of the United States. If, pursuant to such a hearing the final decision rendered in the matter shall affirm the validity and effectiveness of any mining claimant's right or interest under the mining claim as to Leasing Act minerals, then no subsequent proceedings under this section 7 of this Act shall have any force or effect upon the so-affirmed right or interest of such mining claimant under such mining claim. If at any time prior to a hearing the person requesting publication of notice and any person filing a verified statement pursuant to such notice shall so stipulate, then to the extent so stipulated, but only to such extent, no hearing shall be held with respect to rights asserted under that verified statement, and to the extent defined by the stipulation the rights asserted under that verified statement shall be deemed to be unaffected by that particular published notice.

(d) Any person claiming any right in Leasing Act minerals under or by virtue of any unpatented mining claim heretofore located and desiring to receive a copy of any notice of any application, offer, permit, or lease which may be published as above provided in subsection (a) of this section 7, and which may affect lands embraced in such mining claim, may cause to be filed for record in the county office of record where the notice or certificate of location of such mining claim shall have been recorded, a duly acknowledged request for a copy of any such notice. Such request for copies shall set forth the name and address of the person requesting copies and shall also set forth, as to each mining claim under which such person asserts rights in Leasing Act minerals:

(1) the date of location;
(2) the book and page of the recordation of the notice or certificate of location; and
(3) the section or sections of the public land surveys which embrace such mining claim; or if such lands are unsurveyed, either the section or sections which would probably embrace such mining claim when the public land surveys are extended to such lands or a tie by courses and distances to an approved United States mineral monument.

Other than in respect to the requirements of subsection (a) of this section 7 as to personal delivery or mailing of copies of notices and in respect to the provisions of subsection (e) of this section 7, no such request for copies of published notices and no statement or allegation in such request and no recordation thereof shall affect title to any mining claim or to any land or be deemed to constitute constructive notice to any person that the person requesting copies has, or claims, any right, title, or interest in or under any mining claim referred to in such request.

(e) If any applicant, offeror, permittee, or lessee shall fail to comply with the requirements of subsection (a) of this section 7 as to the personal delivery or mailing of a copy of notice to any person, the publication of such notice shall be deemed wholly ineffectual as to that person or as to the rights asserted by that person and the failure of that person to file a verified statement, as provided in such notice, shall in no manner affect, diminish, prejudice or bar any rights of that person.

SEC. 8.   The owner or owners of any mining claim heretofore located Heretofore may, at any time prior to issuance of patent therefor, waive and re- located linquish all rights thereunder to Leasing Act minerals. The execution and claims. acknowledgment of such a waiver and relinquishment by such owner or Relinquish- owners and the recordation thereof in the office where the notice or cer- mineral tificate of location of such mining claim is of record shall render such rights. mining claim thereafter subject to the reservation referred to in section 528 4 of this Act and any patent issued therefor shall contain such a reservation, but no such waiver or relinquishment shall be deemed in any manner to constitute any concession as to the date of priority of rights under said mining claim or as to the validity thereof.

SEC. 9.   Lands withdrawn from the public domain which are within Helium lands (a) Helium Reserve Numbered 1, pursuant to Executive orders of March subject to 21, 1924, and January 28, 1926, and (b) Helium Reserve Numbered 2 entry.

pursuant to Executive Order 6184 of June 26, 1933, shall be subject to entry and location under the mining laws of the United States, and to permit and lease under the mineral leasing laws, upon determination by the Secretary of the Interior, based upon available geologic and other information, that there is no reasonable probability that operations pursuant to entry or location of the particular lands under the mining laws, or pursuant to a permit or lease of the particular lands under the Mineral Leasing Act, will result in the extraction or cause loss or waste of the helium-bearing gas in the lands of such reserves : *Provided*, That the lands shall not become subject to entry, location, permit, or lease until such time as the Secretary designates in an order published in the Federal Register : *And provided further*, That the Secretary may at any time as a condition to continued mineral operations require the entryman, locator, permittee or lessee to take such measures either above or below the surface of the lands as the Secretary deems necessary to prevent loss or waste of the helium-bearing gas.

41 Stat. 437.
30 USC 22,
181 et seq.
Publication
of order
in FR.

SEC. 10.   The Atomic Energy Act is hereby amended as follows :

(a) Section 5 (b) (5) is revised to read :

"(5) ACQUISITION.—The Commission is authorized to the extent it deems necessary to effectuate the provisions of this Act—

60 Stat. 761.
42 USC 1805
(b) (5).
Fissionable
source
materials.

"(A) to purchase, take, requisition, condemn, or otherwise acquire supplies of fissionable source materials or any interest in real property containing deposits of fissionable source materials ; and

"(B) to purchase, take, requisition, condemn, or otherwise acquire rights to enter upon any real property deemed by it to have possibilities of containing deposits of fissionable source materials and to conduct prospecting and exploratory operations for such deposits.

Any purchase made under this paragraph may be made without regard to the provisions of section 3709 of the Revised Statutes (U. S. C., title 41, sec. 5) upon certification by the Commisison that such action is necessary in the interest of the common defense and security, or upon a showing that advertising is not reasonably practicable, and partial and advance payments may be made thereunder. The Commission may establish guaranteed prices for all fissionable source materials delivered to it within a specified time. Just compensation shall be made for any property or interest in property purchased, taken, requisitioned, condemned, or otherwise acquired under this paragraph."

(b) Section 5 (b) (6) is revised to read :

"(6) OPERATIONS ON LANDS BELONGING TO THE UNITED STATES.— The Commission is authorized, to the extent it deems necessary to effectuate the provisions of this Act, to issue leases or permits for prospecting for, exploration for, mining, or removal of deposits of fissionable source materials (or for any or all of these purposes) in lands belonging to the United States : *Provided*, That, notwithstanding any other provisions of law, such leases or permits may be issued for lands administered for national park, monument, and wildlife purposes only when the President, by executive order, finds and declares that such action is necessary in the interests of national defense."

42 USC 1805
(b) (6).

(c) Section 5 (b) (7) is revised to read :

"(7) PUBLIC LANDS.—No individual, corporation, partnership, or association, which had any part, directly or indirectly, in the development of the atomic energy program, may benefit by any location, entry, or settlement upon the public domain made after such individual, corporation, partnership, or association took part in such program, if such individual, corporation, partnership, or association, by reason of having had such part in the development of the atomic energy program, acquired confidential official information as to the existence of deposits of such uranium, thorium, or other fissionable source materials in the specific lands upon which such location, entry, or settlement is made, and subsequent to the date of the enactment of this Act made such location, entry, or settlement or cause the same to be made for his, or its, or their benefit. In cases where any patent, conveyance, lease, permit, or other authorization has

42 USC 1805
(b) (7).

been issued, which reserved to the United States fissionable source materials and the right to enter upon the land and prospect for, mine, and remove the same, the head of the department or agency which issued the patent, conveyance, lease, permit, or other authorization shall, on application of the holder thereof, issue a new or supplemental patent, conveyance, lease, permit, or other authorization without such reservation."

(d) Notwithstanding the provisions of the Atomic Energy Act, and 42 USC 1801 particularly section 5 (b) (7) thereof, prior to its amendment hereby, or note Supra. the provisions of the Act of August 12, 1953 (67 Stat. 539), and particu- 30 USC 501- larly section 3 thereof, any mining claim, heretofore located under the 505. mining laws of the United States, for, or based upon a discovery of a 30 USC 503. mineral deposit which is a fissionable source material and which, except for the possible contrary construction of said Atomic Energy Act, would have been locatable under such mining laws, shall, insofar as adversely affected by such possible contrary construction, be valid and effective, in all respects to the same extent as if said mineral deposit were a locatable mineral deposit other than a fissionable source material.

SEC. 11. As used in this Act "mineral leasing laws" shall mean the "Mineral Act of October 20, 1914 (38 Stat. 741); the Act of February 25, 1920 leasing (41 Stat. 437); the Act of April 17, 1926 (44 Stat. 301); the Act of 48 USC 22- February 7, 1927 (44 Stat. 1057); and all Acts heretofore or hereafter 287, passim. enacted which are amendatory of or supplementary to any of the foregoing Acts: "Leasing Act minerals" shall mean all minerals which, upon the "Leasing Act effective date of this Act, are provided in the mineral leasing laws to be minerals." disposed of thereunder; "Leasing Act operations" shall mean operations "Leasing Act conducted under a lease, permit, or license issued under the mineral operations." leasing laws in or incidental to prospecting for, drilling for, mining, treating, storing, transporting, or removing Leasing Act minerals; "mining "Mining operations" shall mean operations under any unpatented or patented operations." mining claim or millsite in or incidental to prospecting for, mining, treat- 30 U.S.C.A. ing, storing, transporting, or removing minerals other than Leasing Act 530 minerals and any other use under any claim of right or title based upon such mining claim or millsite; "Leasing Act operator" shall mean any "Leasing Act party who shall conduct Leasing Act operations; "mining operator" shall operations." mean any party who shall conduct mining operations; "Atomic Energy "Mining operator." Act" shall mean the Act of August 1, 1946 (60 Stat. 755), as amended; 42 USC 1801 "Atomic Energy Commission" shall mean the United States Atomic En- note. ergy Commission established under the Atomic Energy Act or any amend- "AEC." ments thereof; "fissionable source material" shall mean uranium, thorium, "Fissionable and all other materials referred to in section 5 (b) (1) of the Atomic source Energy Act as reserved or to be reserved to the United States; "uranium material." lease application" shall mean an application for a uranium lease filed 42 USC 1805 with said Commission with respect to lands which would be open for entry (b) (1). under the mining laws except for their being lands embraced within an "Uranium lease appli- offer, application, permit, or lease under the mineral leasing laws or lands cation." known to be valuable for minerals leasable under those laws; "uranium "Uranium lease" shall mean a uranium mining lease issued by said Commission with lease." respect to any such lands; and "person" shall mean any individual, corpo- "Person." ration, partnership, or other legal entity.

SEC. 12. Nothing in this Act shall be construed to waive, amend, or Requirement. repeal the requirement of any provision of any law for approval of any 30 U.S.C.A. official of the United States whose approval prior to prospecting, ex- 531 ploring, or mining would be required.

SEC. 13. If any provision of this Act, or the application of such pro- Separability. vision to any person or circumstances, is held unconstitutional, invalid, or 30 U.S.C.A. unenforcible, the remainder of this Act or the application of such provi- 521 note sion to persons or circumstances other than those as to which it is held unconstitutional, invalid, or unenforcible, shall not be affected thereby.

Approved August 13, 1954.

PUBLIC LAW 167

Changes in the basic mining law became effective on July 23, 1955, when President Eisenhower signed a bill amending the mining laws and the Materials Disposal Act. Known as Public Law 167, 84th Congress, 1st Session, the bill excludes certain nonmetallic materials from mineral location and affects the surface rights of claims filed in the future. It does not apply to valid claims existing prior to the time the act became law.

In brief, this law makes the following provisions: (1) Bans the location of mining claims for common varieties of sand, stone, gravel, pumice, pumicite, and cinders, and makes them subject to disposal under the Materials Disposal Act. It will not affect the validity of any mining location based upon discovery of some other mineral occurring in or in association with such deposits. Also, deposits of the above materials which are valuable because of certain properties giving them distinct and special value would continue to be locatable. (2) Prohibits the use of mining claims hereafter located and prior to patent, for any purpose other than prospecting, mining, processing, and related activities. (3) Authorizes the federal government, on claims hereafter located and prior to patent, to manage and dispose of timber and forage, and bars the claimant from removing or using the timber or other surface resources except as needed for mining activity. (4) Provides a procedure under which the federal government can resolve title uncertainties resulting from the existence of abandoned invalid, dormant, or unidentifiable mining claims located prior to the enactment of this measure. In view of its importance, the bill has been reproduced below in its entirety. See discussion in guide, pages 14-15.

Public Law 167—84th Congress
Chapter 375—1st Session

H. R. 5891

AN ACT

To amend the Act of July 31, 1947 (61 Stat. 681) and the mining laws to provide for multiple use of the surface of the same tracts of the public lands, and for other purposes.

Be it enacted by the Senate and House of Representatives of the United
Public lands. *States of America in Congress assembled,* That section 1 of the Act of
43 USC July 31, 1947 (61 Stat. 681), is amended to read as follows:
1185.
Materials   "Section 601. The Secretary, under such rules and regulations as he
disposal.   may prescribe, may dispose of mineral materials (including but not limited
30 U.S.C.A.   to common varieties of the following: sand, stone, gravel, pumice, pumicite,
601   cinders, and clay) and vegetative materials (including but not limited to
              yucca, manzanita, mesquite, cactus, and timber or other forest products)
              on public lands of the United States, including, for the purposes of this
43 USC   Act, land described in Section 1181a-1181j of Title 43, if the disposal of
1181a-   such mineral or vegetative materials (1) is not otherwise expressly au-
1181j.   thorized by law, including, but not limited to, Sections 315-315m, 315n,
43 USC 315   315o-l, and 1171 of Title 43, as amended, and the United States Mining
et seq., 1171. laws, and (2) is not expressly prohibited by laws of the United States,
              and (3) would not be detrimental to the public interest. Such materials
              may be disposed of only in accordance with the provisions of this Act and
              upon the payment of adequate compensation therefor, to be determined by
              the Secretary: *Provided, however,* That, to the extent not otherwise
              authorized by law, the Secretary is authorized in his discretion to permit
              any Federal, State, or Territorial agency, unit or subdivision, including
              municipalities, or any association or corporation not organized for profit,

to take and remove, without charge, materials and resources subject to this Act, for use other than for commercial or industrial purposes or resale. Where the lands have been withdrawn in aid of a funtcion of a Federal department or agency other than the department headed by the Secretary or of a State, Territory, county, municipality, water district or other local governmental subdivision or agency, the Secretary may make disposals under this Act only with the consent of such other Federal department or agency or of such State, Territory, or local governmental unit. Nothing in this Act shall be construed to apply to lands in any national park, or national monument or to any Indian lands, or lands set aside or held for the use or benefit of Indians, including lands over which jurisdiction has been transferred to the Department of the Interior by Executive order for the use of Indians. As used in this Act, the word "Secretary" means the Secretary of the Interior except that it means the Secretary of Agriculture where the lands involved are administered by him for national forest purposes or for the purposes of Sections 1010-1012 of Title 7 or where withdrawn for the purpose of any other function of the Department of Agriculture."   50 Stat. 525. 7 USC 1010 et seq.

SEC. 603.   43 USC 1187.
"All moneys received from the disposal of materials under this Act shall be disposed of in the same manner as moneys received from the sale of public lands, except that moneys received from the disposal of materials by the Secretary of Agriculture shall be disposed of in the same manner as other moneys received by the Department of Agriculture from the administration of the lands from which the disposal of materials is made, and except that revenues from the lands described in the Sections 1181a-1181j of Title 43 shall be disposed of in accordance with said sections and except that moneys received from the disposal of materials from school section lands in Alaska, reserved under section 353 of Title 48 shall be set apart as separate and permanent funds in the Territorial Treasury, as provided for income derived from said school section lands pursuant to said Act."   Moneys received. 69 Stat.367. 69 Stat.368. 30 U.S.C.A. 603   43 USC 1181a-1181j.   48 USC 353.

SEC. 611.   A deposit of common varieties of sand, stone, gravel, pumice, pumicite, or cinders shall not be deemed a valuable mineral deposit within the meaning of the mining laws of the United States so as to give effective validity to any mining claim hereafter located under such mining laws: *Provided, however,* That nothing herein shall affect the validity of any mining location based upon discovery of some other mineral occuring in or in association with such a deposit. "Common varieties" as used in sections 601, 603, and 611-615 of this Title does not include deposits of such materials which are valuable because the deposit has some property giving it distinct and special value and does not include so-called "block pumice" which occurs in nature in pieces having one dimension of two inches or more.   Common varieties.

SEC. 612.   (a) Any mining claim hereafter located under the mining laws of the United States shall not be used, prior to issuance of patent therefor, for any purposes other than prospecting, mining or processing operations and uses reasonably incident thereto.   Unpatented mining claims. Restrictions.
(b) Rights under any mining claim hereafter located under the mining laws of the United States shall be subject, prior to issuance of patent therefor, to the right of the United States to manage and dispose of the vegetative surface resources thereof and to manage other surface resources thereof (except mineral deposits subject to location under the mining laws of the United States). Any such mining claim shall also be subject, prior to issuance of patent therefor, to the right of the United States, its permittees, and licensees, to use so much of the surface thereof as may be necessary for such purposes or for access to adjacent land: *Provided, however,* That any use of the surface of any such mining claim by the United States, its permittees or licensees, shall be such as not to endanger or materially interfere with prospecting, mining or processing operations or uses reasonably incident thereto: *Provided, further,* That if at any time the locator requires more timber for his mining operations than is available to him from the claim after disposition of timber therefrom by the   Timber.

United States, subsequent to the location of the claim, he shall be entitled, free of charge, to be supplied with timber for such requirements from the nearest timber administered by the disposing agency which is ready for harvesting under the rules and regulations of that agency and which is substantially equivalent in kind and quantity to the timber estimated by the disposing agency to have been disposed of from the claim: *Provided, further,* That nothing in sections 601, 603, and 611-615 of this Title shall be construed as affecting or intended to affect or in any way interfere with or modify the laws of the States which lie wholly or in part westward of the ninety-eighth meridian relating to the ownership, control, appropriation, use, and distribution of ground or surface waters within any unpatented mining claim.

69 Stat. 368.
69 Stat. 369.

(c) Except to the extent required for the mining claimant's prospecting, mining or processing operations and uses reasonably incident thereto, or for the construction of buildings or structures in connection therewith, or to provide clearance for such operations or uses, or to the extent authorized by the United States, no claimant of any mining claim hereafter located under the mining laws of the United States shall, prior to issuance of patent therefor, sever, remove, or use any vegetative or other surface resources thereof which are subject to management or disposition by the United States under the preceding subsection (b). Any severance or removal of timber which is permitted under the exceptions of the preceding sentence, other than severance or removal to provide clearance, shall be in accordance with sound principles of forest management.

Notices to mining claimants. Publication.

SEC. 613. (a) The head of a Federal department or agency which has the responsibility for administering surface resources of any lands belonging to the United States may file as to such lands in the office of the Secretary of the Interior, or in such office as the Secretary of the Interior may designate, a request for publication of notice to mining claimants, for determination of surface rights, which request shall contain a description of the lands covered thereby, showing the section or sections of the public land surveys which embrace the lands covered by such request, or if such lands are unsurveyed, either the section or sections which would probably embrace such lands when the public land surveys are extended to such lands or a tie by courses and distances to an approved United States mineral monument.

The filing of such request for publication shall be accompanied by an affidavit or affidavits of a person or persons over twenty-one years of age setting forth that the affiant or affiants have examined the lands involved in a reasonable effort to ascertain whether any person or persons were in actual possession of or engaged in the working of such lands or any part thereof, and, if no person or persons were found to be in actual possession of or engaged in the working of said lands or any part thereof on the date of such examination, setting forth such fact, or, if any person or persons were so found to be in actual posession or engaged in such working on the date of such examination, setting forth the name and address of each such person, unless affiant shall have been unable through reasonable inquiry to obtain information as to the name and address of any such person, in which event the affidavit shall set forth fully the nature and results of such inquiry.

The filing of such request for publication shall also be accompanied by the certificate of a title or abstract company, or of a title abstractor, or of an attorney, based upon such company's abstractor's, or attorney's examination of those instruments which are shown by the tract indexes in the county office of record as effecting the lands described in said request, setting forth the name of any person disclosed by said instruments to have an interest in said lands under any unpatented mining claim heretofore located, together with the address of such person if such address is disclosed by such instruments of record. "Tract indexes" as used herein shall mean those indexes, if any, as to surveyed lands identifying instruments as affecting a particular legal subdivision of the public land surveys, and as to unsurveyed lands identifying instruments as affecting a particular probable legal subdivision according to a projected extension of the public land surveys.

Thereupon the Secretary of the Interior, at the expense of the request- 69 Stat. 369.
ing department or agency, shall cause notice to mining claimants to be 69 Stat. 370.
published in a newspaper having general circulation in the county in which
the lands involved are situate.

Such notice shall describe the lands covered by such request, as provided
heretofore, and shall notify whomever it may concern that if any person
claiming or asserting under, or by virtue of, any unpatented mining claim
heretofore located, rights as to such lands of any part thereof, shall fail
to file in the office where such request for publication was filed (which
office shall be specified in such notice) and within one hundred and fifty
days from the date of the first publication of such notice (which date shall
be specified in such notice), a verified statement which shall set forth, as
to such unpatented mining claim—

(1) the date of location;
(2) the book and page of recordation of the notice or certificate
of location;
(3) the section or sections of the public land surveys which embrace such mining claims; or if such lands are unsurveyed, either
the section or sections which would probably embrace such mining
claim when the public land surveys are extended to such lands or a
tie by courses and distances to an approved United States mineral
monument;
(4) whether such claimant is a locator or purchaser under such
location; and
(5) the name and address of such claimant and names and addresses so far as known to the claimant of any other person or persons claiming any interest or interests in or under such unpatented
mining claim;

such failure shall be conclusively deemed (i) to constitute a waiver and
relinquishment by such mining claimant of any right, title, or interest
under such mining claim contrary to or in conflict with the limitations or
restrictions specified in section 4 of this Act as to hereafter located unpatented mining claims, and (ii) to constitute a consent by such mining
claimant that such mining claim, prior to issuance of patent therefor, shall
be subject to the limitations and restrictions specified in section 4 of this
Act as to hereafter located unpatented mining claims, and (iii) to preclude thereafter, prior to issuance of patent, any assertion by such mining
claimant of any right or title to or interest in or under such mining claim
contrary to or in conflict with the limitations or restrictions specified in
section 4 of this Act as to hereafter located unpatented mining claims.

If such notice is published in a daily paper, it shall be published in the
Wednesday issue for nine consecutive weeks, or, if in a weekly paper, in
nine consecutive issues, or if in a semiweekly or triweekly paper, in the
issue of the same day of each week for nine consecutive weeks.

Within fifteen days after the date of first publication of such notice,
the department or agency requesting such publication (1) shall cause a
copy of such notice to be personally delivered to or to be mailed by registered mail addressed to each person in possession or engaged in the working of the land whose name and address is shown by an affidavit filed as
aforesaid, and to each person who may have filed, as to any lands described
in said notice, a request for notices, as provided in subsection (d) of this
section 5, and shall cause a copy of such notice to be mailed by registered
mail to each person whose name and address is set forth in the title or
abstract company's or title abstractor's or attorney's certificate filed as 69 Stat. 370.
aforesaid, as having an interest in the lands described in said notice under 69 Stat. 371.
any unpatented mining claim heretofore located, such notice to be directed
to such person's address as set forth in such certificate; and (2) shall file
in the office where said request for publication was filed an affidavit showing that copies have been so delivered or mailed.

(b) If any claimant under any unpatented mining claim heretofore Failure to
located which embraces any of the lands described in any notice published file verified
in accordance with the provisions of subsection (a) of this section 5, shall statement.

fail to file a verified statement, as above provided, within one hundred and fifty days from the date of the first publication of such notice, such failure shall be conclusively deemed, except as otherwise provided in subsection (e) of this section 5, (i) to constitute a waiver and relinquishment by such mining claimant of any right, title, or interest under such mining claim contrary to or in conflict with the limitations or restrictions specified in section 4 of this Act as to hereafter located unpatented mining claims, and (ii) to constitute a consent by such mining claimant that such mining claim, prior to issuance of patent therefor, shall be subject to the limitations and restrictions specified in section 4 of this Act as to hereafter located unpatented mining claims, and (iii) to preclude thereafter, prior to issuance of patent, any assertion by such mining claimant of any right or title to or interest in or under such mining claim contrary to or in conflict with the limitations or restrictions specified in section 4 of this Act as to hereafter located unpatented mining claims.

Hearings.   (c) If any verified statement shall be filed by a mining claimant as provided in subsection (a) of this section 5, then the Secretary of Interior shall fix a time and place for a hearing to determine the validity and effectiveness of any right or title to, or interest in or under such mining claim, which the mining claimant may assert contrary to or in conflict with the limitations and restrictions specified in section 4 of this Act as to hereafter located unpatented mining claims, which place of hearing shall be in the county where the lands in question or parts thereof are located, unless the mining claimant agrees otherwise. Where verified statements are filed asserting rights to an aggregate of more than twenty mining claims, any single hearing shall be limited to a maximum of twenty mining claims unless the parties affected shall otherwise stipulate and as many separate hearings shall be set as shall be necessary to comply with this provision. The procedures with respect to notice of such a hearing and the conduct thereof, and in respect to appeals shall follow the then established general procedures and rules of practice of the Department of the Interior in respect to contests or protests affecting public lands of the United States. If, pursuant to such a hearing the final decision rendered in the matter shall affirm the validity and effectiveness of any mining claimant's so asserted right or interest under the mining claim, then no subsequent proceedings under this section 5 of this Act shall have any force or effect upon the so-affirmed right or interest of such mining claimant under such mining claim. If at any time prior to a hearing the department or agency requesting publication of notice and any person filing a verified statement pursuant to such notice shall so stipulate, then to the extent so stipulated, but only to such extent, no hearing shall be held with respect to rights asserted under that verified statement, and to the extent defined by the stipulation the rights asserted under that verified statement shall be deemed to be unaffected by that particular published notice.

Requests for copies of notices.
69 Stat. 371.
69 Stat. 372.   (d) Any person claiming any right under or by virtue of any unpatented mining claim heretofore located and desiring to receive a copy of any notice to mining claimants which may be published as above provided in subsection (a) of this section 5, and which may affect lands embraced in such mining claim, may cause to be filed for record in the county office of record where the notice or certificate of location of such mining claim shall have been recorded, a duly acknowledged request for a copy of any such notice. Such request for copies shall set forth the name and address of the person requesting copies and shall also set forth, as to each heretofore located unpatented mining claim under which such person asserts rights—

          (1) the date of location;
          (2) the book and page of the recordation of the notice or certificate of location; and
          (3) the section or sections of the public land surveys which embrace such mining claim; or if such lands are unsurveyed, either the section or sections which would probably embrace such mining claim when the public land surveys are extended to such lands or a tie by courses and distances to an approved United States mineral monument.

Other than in respect to the requirements of subsection (a) of this section 5 as to personal delivery or mailing of copies of notices and in respect to the provisions of subsection (e) of this section 5, no such request for copies of published notices and no statement or allegation in such request and no recordation thereof shall affect title to any mining claim or to any land or be deemed to constitute constructive notice to any person that the person requesting copies has, or claims, any right, title, or interest in or under any mining claim referred to in such request.

(e) If any department or agency requesting publication shall fail to comply with the requirements of subsection (a) of this section 5 as to the personal delivery or mailing of a copy of notice to any person, the publication of such notice shall be deemed wholly ineffectual as to that person or as to the rights asserted by that person and the failure of that person to file a verified statement, as provided in such notice, shall in no manner affect, diminish, prejudice or bar any rights of that person. **Failure to meet notice requirements.**

SEC. 614. The owner or owners of any unpatented mining claim here-tofore located may waive and relinquish all rights thereunder which are contrary to or in conflict with the limitations or restrictions specified in section 612 of this Title as to hereafter located unpatented mining claims. The execution and acknowledgment of such a waiver and relinquishment by such owner or owners and the recordation thereof in the office where the notice or certificate of location of such mining claim is of record shall render such mining claim thereafter and prior to issuance of patent subject to the limitations and restrictions in section 612 of this Title in all respects as if said mining claim had been located after enactment of sections 601, 603, and 611-615 of this title, but no such waiver or relinquishment shall be deemed in any manner to constitute any concession as to the date of priority of rights under said mining claim or as to the validity thereof. **Waiver of rights.**

SEC. 615. Nothing in sections 601, 603, and 611-615 of this Title shall be construed in any manner to limit or restrict or to authorize the limitation or restriction of any existing rights of any claimant under any valid mining claim heretofore located, except as such rights may be limited or restricted as a result of a proceeding pursuant to section 613 of this Title, or as a result of a waiver and relinquishment pursuant to section 614 of this Title; and nothing in 601, 603, and 611-615 of this Title shall be construed in any manner to authorize inclusion in any patent hereafter issued under the mining laws of the United States for any mining claim heretofore or hereafter located, of any reservation, limitation, or restriction not otherwise authorized by law, or to limit or repeal any existing authority to include any reservation, limitation, or restriction in any patent, or to limit or restrict any use of the lands covered by any patented or unpatented mining claim by the United States, its lessees, permittees, and licensees which is otherwise authorized by law. **Limitation of existing rights, etc.** **69 Stat.372. 69 Stat.373.**

Approved July 23, 1955.

PUBLIC LAW 359

Public Law 359, alters the mining laws on public lands set aside for power development. See discussion in guide, pages 15-16.

Public Law 359—84th Congress
Chapter 797—1st Session
H. R. 100

AN ACT

To permit the mining, development, and utilization of the mineral resources of all public lands withdrawn or reserved for power development, and for other purposes.

Be it enacted by the Senate and House of Representatives of the United States of America in Congress assembled, That this Act may be cited as the "Mining Claims Rights Restoration Act of 1955."

30 U.S.C.A.
621

SEC. 621. All public lands belonging to the United States heretofore, now or hereafter withdrawn or reserved for power development or power sites shall be open to entry for location and patent of mining claims and for mining, development, beneficiation, removal, and utilization of the mineral resources of such lands under applicable Federal statutes: *Provided*, That all power rights to such lands shall be retained by the United States: *Provided further*, That locations made under this Act within the revested Oregon and California Railroad and reconveyed Coos Bay Wagon grant lands shall also be subject to the provisions of the Act of April 8, 1948, Public Law 477 (Eightieth Congress, second session) : *And provided further*, That nothing contained herein shall be constituted to open for the purposes described in this section any lands (1) which are included in any project operating or being constructed under a license or permit issued under the Federal Power Act or other Act of Congress, or (2) which are under examination and survey by a prospective licensee of the Federal Power Commission, if such prospective licensee holds an uncanceled preliminary permit issued under the Federal Power Act authorizing him to conduct such examination and survey with respect to such lands and such permit has not been renewed in the case of such prospective licensee more than once.

(b) The locator of a placer claim under this Act, however, shall conduct no mining operations for a period of sixty days after the filing of a notice of location pursuant to section 4 of this Act. If the Secretary of the Interior, within sixty days from the filing of the notice of location, notifies the locator by registered mail of the Secretary's intention to hold a public hearing to determine whether placer mining operations would substantially interfere with other uses of the land included within the placer claim, mining operations on that claim shall be further suspended until the Secretary has held the hearing and has issued an appropriate order. The order issued by the Secretary of the Interior shall provide for one of the following: (1) a complete prohibition of placer mining; (2) a permission to engage in placer mining upon the condition that the locator shall, following placer operations, restore the surface of the claim to the condition in which it was immediately prior to those operations; or (3) a general permission to engage in placer mining. No order by the Secretary with respect to such operations shall be valid unless a certified copy is filed in the same State or county office in which the locator's notice of location has been filed in compliance with the United States mining laws.

The Secretary shall establish such rules and regulations as he deems desirable concerning bonds and deposits with respect to the restoration of lands to their condition prior to placer mining operations. Moneys received from any bond or deposit shall be used for the restoration of the surface of the claim involved, and any money received in excess of the amount needed for the restoration of the surface of that claim shall be refunded.

(c) Nothing in this Act shall affect the validity of withdrawals or reservations for purposes other than power development.

30 U.S.C.A.
622

SEC. 622. Prospecting and exploration for and the development and utilization of mineral resources authorized in this Act shall be entered into or continued at the financial risk of the individual party or parties undertaking such work: *Provided*, That the United States, its permittees and licensees shall not be responsible or held liable or incur any liability for the damage, destruction, or loss of any mining claim, mill site, facility installed or erected, income, or other property or investments resulting from the actual use of such lands or portions thereof for power development at any time where such power development is made by or under the authority of the United States, except where such damage, destruction, or loss results from the negligence of the United States, its permittees and licensees.

30 U.S.C.A.
623

SEC. 623. The owner of any unpatented mining claim located on land described in section 621 of this Act shall file for record in the United States district land office of the land district in which the claim is situated (1) within one year after August 11, 1955, as to any or all locations heretofore made, or within sixty days of location as to locations hereafter made, a copy of the notice of location of the claim; (2) within sixty days after the expiration of any annual assessment year, a statement as to the assessment work done or improvements made during the previous assessment year.

SEC. 624. Nothing in this Act contained shall be construed to limit or restrict the rights of the owner or owners of any valid mining claim located prior to the date of withdrawal or reservation: *Provided*, That nothing in this Act shall be construed to limit or restrict the rights of the owner or owners of any mining claim who are diligently working to make a discovery of valuable minerals at the time any future withdrawal or reservation for power development is made. 30 USCA 624

SEC. 625. Notwithstanding any other provisions of this Act, all mining claims and mill sites or mineral rights located under the terms of this Act or otherwise contained on the public lands as described in section 2 shall be used only for the purposes specified in section 2 and no facility or activity shall be erected or conducted thereon for other purposes. 30 USCA 625

Approved August 11, 1955.

PUBLIC LAW 876

This statute, approved September 2, 1958, provides that geological, geophysical and geochemical surveys conducted by qualified experts may be considered as labor with respect to the annual assessment work requirements for unpatented mining claims.

Public Law 85-876
85th Congress, S. 2039
September 2, 1958

AN ACT

To clarify the requirements with respect to the performance of labor imposed as a condition for the holding of mining claims on Federal lands pending the issuance of patents therefor. 72 Stat. 1701

Be it enacted by the Senate and House of Representatives of the United States of America in Congress assembled, That the term "labor", as used in the third sentence of section 2324 of the Revised Statutes (30 U.S.C. 28), shall include, without being limited to, geological, geochemical and geophysical surveys conducted by qualified experts and verified by a detailed report filed in the county office in which the claim is located which sets forth fully (a) the location of the work performed in relation to the point of discovery and boundaries of the claim, (b) the nature, extent, and cost thereof, (c) the basic findings therefrom, and (d) the name, address, and professional background of the person or persons conducting the work. Such surveys, however, may not be applied as labor for more than two consecutive years or for more than a total of five years on any one mining claim, and each such survey shall be nonrepetitive of any previous survey on the same claim. Mining claims, labor requirements

SEC. 2. As used in this Act,

(a) The term "geological surveys" means surveys on the ground for mineral deposits by the proper application of the principles and techniques of the science of geology as they relate to the search for and discovery of mineral deposits; Definitions

(b) The term "geochemical surveys" means surveys on the ground for mineral deposits by the proper application of the principles and techniques of the science of chemistry as they relate to the search for and discovery of mineral deposits;

(c) The term "geophysical surveys" means surveys on the ground for mineral deposits through the employment of generally recognized equipment and methods for measuring physical differences between rock types or discontinuities in geological formations;

(d) The term "qualified expert" means an individual qualified by education or experience to conduct geological, geochemical or geophysical surveys, as the case may be.

Approved September 2, 1958.

PUBLIC LAW 390
S. 2033

On March 18, 1960, a statute was approved that permits the location and patenting of a mill site in connection with a placer claim or claims. Section 2337 of the Revised Statutes of the United States (30 U.S.C. 42) is amended (1) by adding "(a)" after "Sec. 2337.", and (2) by adding at the end thereof a new subsection as follows:

"(b) Where nonmineral land is needed by the proprietor of a placer claim for mining, milling, processing, beneficiation, or other operations in connection with such claim, and is used or occupied by the proprietor for such purposes, such land may be included in an application for a patent for such claim, and may be patented therewith subject to the same requirements as to survey and notice as are applicable to placers. No location made of such nonmineral land shall exceed five acres and payment for the same shall be made at the rate applicable to placer claims which do not include a vein or lode." (PUBLIC LAW 86-390; 74 STAT. 7, approved March 18, 1960.)

FISH AND GAME CODE CHANGES, 1961

Section 1505 of the Code provides that the Department of Fish and Game "may manage, control and protect" fish spawning areas in specified portions of the following rivers: American, Feather, Merced, Mokelumne, Sacramento, Stanislaus, Tuolumne and Yuba. Activities to be "controlled" include "—removing of materials from the streambeds in the areas designated in this section, other than as necessary for the installation of structures."

Sections 1601 and 1602, Chapter 6, Division 2 of the Code require that anyone engaged in activities that change the bed, channel or bank of any river, stream or lake, or use any material from the streambed shall notify the department and receive the department's recommendations for protecting the fish and wildlife resources. Anyone "proposing to conduct new operations of this type shall not commence such operations until such recommendations have been received."

Section 5653 of the California Fish and Game Code, of particular interest to persons skin diving for gold, reads as follows:

"Before any person uses any vacuum or suction dredge equipment in any river, stream, or lake of this State, he shall submit an application to the Department of Fish and Game specifying the type and size of equipment to be used and the locations where such equipment will be used.

"If the department determines that such operation will not be deleterious to fish it shall issue a permit to the applicant. If the applicant operates any equipment other than that specified in the permit or conducts such operation outside of the area designated in the permit, or if any person conducts such operation without securing such permit, he shall be guilty of a misdemeanor."

Further information on any of these code sections, and applications and permits under section 5653 may be obtained from the following offices of the Department:

REGION I   627 Cypress St., Redding (Del Norte, Humboldt, Lassen, Modoc, Shasta, Siskiyou, Tehama, Trinity Counties)

REGION II   1001 Jedsmith Dr., Sacramento (Alpine, Amador, Butte, Calaveras, Colusa, El Dorado, Glenn, Nevada, Placer, Plumas, Sacramento, San Joaquin, Sierra, Solano, Sutter, Yolo, Yuba Counties)

REGION III Ferry Building, San Francisco (Alameda, Contra Costa, Lake, Marin, Mendocino, Monterey, Napa, San Benito, San Francisco, Santa Cruz, San Luis Obispo, San Mateo, Santa Clara, Sonoma Counties)

REGION IV 1234 E. Shaw, Fresno (Fresno, Kern, Kings, Madera, Mariposa, Merced, Tulare, Tuolumne, Stanislaus Counties)

REGION V 217 W. First St., Los Angeles (Imperial, Inyo, Los Angeles, Mono, Orange, Riverside, San Bernardino, Santa Barbara, San Diego, Ventura Counties)

SPECIAL REGULATIONS GOVERNING MINING IN DEATH VALLEY NATIONAL MONUMENT

Death Valley is the only National Monument in California in which prospecting and mining is permitted. Administrative regulations governing such activities in the Monument are contained in Chapter I, Title 36 of the Code of Federal Regulations, pertinent portions of which are printed below.

7.26. *Death Valley National Monument*—(a) *Mining.* Mining in Death Valley National Monument is subject to the following regulations, which are prescribed to govern the surface use of claims therein:

(1) The claim shall be occupied and used exclusively for mineral exploration and development and for no other purpose except that upon written permission of an authorized officer or employee of the National Park Service the surface of the claim may be used for other specified purposes, the use to be on such conditions and for such period as may be prescribed when permission is granted.

(2) The owner of the claim and all persons holding under him shall conform to all rules and regulations governing occupancy of the lands within the National Monument.

(3) The use and occupancy of the surface of mining claims as prescribed in subparagraph (1) and (2) of the paragraph shall apply to all such claims located after the date of the Act of June 13, 1933 (48 Stat. 139, 16 U.S.C. 447), within the limits of the National Monument as fixed by Proclamation No. 2028 of February 11, 1933, and enlarged by Proclamation No. 2228 of March 26, 1937, and to all mining claims on lands hereafter included in the National Monument, located after such inclusion so long as such claims are within the boundaries of said Monument.

(4) Prospectors or miners shall not open or construct roads or vehicle trails without first obtaining written permission from an authorized officer or employee of the National Park Service. Applications for permits shall be accompanied by a map or sketch showing the location of the mining property to be served and the location of the proposed road or vehicle trail. The permit shall be conditioned upon the permittee's maintaining the road or trail in a passable condition as long as it is used by the permittee or his successors.

(5) From and after the date of publication of this section, no construction, development, or dumping upon any location or entry, lying wholly or partly within the areas set forth in subdivisions (i) to (iii) of this subparagraph, shall be undertaken until the plans for such construction, development, and dumping insofar as the surface is affected thereby, shall have been first submitted to and approved in writing by an authorized officer or employee of the National Park Service.

(i) All land within 200 feet of the center line of any public road.

(ii) All land within the smallest legal subdivision of the public land surveys containing a spring or waterhole or within one quarter of a mile thereof on unsurveyed public land.

(iii) All land within any site developed or approved for development by National Park Service as a residential, administrative, or public campground site. Such sites shall include all land within the exterior boundaries thereof as conspicuously posted by the placing of an appropriate sign disclosing that the boundaries of the developed site are designated on a map of the site which will be available for inspection in the office of the Superintendent. If not so posted, such sites shall include all land within 1,000 feet of any Federally owned buildings, water and sewer systems, road loops, and camp tables and fireplaces set at designated camp sites.

(b) *Use of Water.* No works or water system of any kind for the diversion, impoundment, appropriation, transmission or other use of water shall be constructed on or across Monument lands, including mining claims, without a permit approved by an authorized officer or employee of the National Park Service. Application for such permit shall be accompanied by plans of the proposed construction. The permit shall contain the following conditions: (1) No diversion and use of the water shall conflict with the paramount general public need for such water; (2) Such water systems shall include taps or spigots at points to be prescribed by the Superintendent, for the convenience of the public; and (3) All appropriations of water, in compliance with the State water laws, shall be made for public use in the name of the United States and in accordance with instructions to be supplied by an authorized officer or employee of the National Park Service.

(c) *Permits*. Application for any permit required by this section shall be made through the Superintendent, Death Valley National Monument, Death Valley, California.

(d) *Filing of copies of mining locations*. From and after the publication of this paragraph, in order to facilitate the administration of the regulations in this part, copies of all mining locations filed in the office of the County Recorder shall be furnished to the office of the Superintendent, Death Valley National Monument, by the person filing the mining location in his own behalf or on behalf of any other person.

Section 1.91, paragraph (a) of the General Rules and Regulations, *Penalties* states: "Any person who violates any provision of the rules and regulations in this chapter, or as the same may be amended or supplemented . . . shall be deemed guilty of a misdemeanor and upon conviction thereof shall be punished by a fine of not more than $500 or imprisonment for not exceeding 6 months, or both, and be adjudged to pay all costs of the proceedings."

DIAGRAM OF A SECTION
I SQUARE MILE-640 ACRES

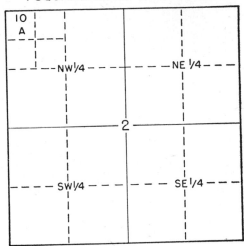

DIAGRAM OF A TOWNSHIP
36 SECTIONS

36	31	32	33	34	35	36	31
I	6	5	4	3	2	I	6
12	7	8	9	10	11	12	7
13	18	17	16	15	14	13	18
24	19	20	21	22	23	24	19
25	30	29	28	27	26	25	30
36	31	32	33	34	35	36	31

TOWNSHIP LINE

| I | 6 | 5 | 4 | 3 | 2 | I | 6 |

RANGE LINE

Diagram of a section; diagram of a township.

APPENDIX II

COMMENT BY THE REVISOR, CHARLES L. GILMORE

It must be recognized that honest differences of opinion exist in legal matters as well as in all other human activities. The Division of Mines does not have an attorney on its staff and is, therefore, not in a position to make a statement of official opinion on controversial legal matters. The following commentary by the revisor of this edition of the Legal Guide, Mr. Charles L. Gilmore, represents his personal opinions on a few of the controversial aspects of mining law and of other factors affecting the citizens' rights to locatable minerals in public lands. These opinions are based upon many years of experience in the practice of mining law, and are presented here for whatever interest and value they may have to readers of the Legal Guide.

A. (refer to page 14 in text)

In commenting upon the regulations set forth by the Bureau of Land Management, Mr. Gilmore states, "The statute itself designates the classifications of mineral materials and vegetative materials, and their disposal is under such rules and regulations as the Secretary may prescribe. In other words, the Secretary may prescribe the form and the manner, and perhaps the price, at which these mineral materials, including but not limited to common varieties of sand, stone, gravel, pumice, pumicite, cinders and clay, and vegetative materials including but not limited to yucca, manzanita, mesquite, cactus and timber and other forest products on public lands of the United States, may be disposed of, but I can find nothing in the whole act that gives the Secretary of the Interior the final authority to determine whether a given material comes under the act or whether it is subject to evidentiary proof on the character. In other words, I find nothing in this act or in any decision of any court of which I am aware at present that says that, without evidence as to character or value or both, the Secretary of the Interior may without hearing determine arbitrarily whether a given deposit comes within the purview of the act.

There is a difference between regulations providing for administration and regulations that determine the rights of the citizen to private property. In the one, as long as the regulations follow the law, they will be upheld, but in the latter instance the cases are quite numerous where the regulation has been found invalid as being in excess of the power of the Secretary of the Interior or his subordinates.

What is a common variety is a question of fact determinable from the conditions peculiar to a particular deposit and its proximity to a commercial use site."

B. (refer to page 15 in text)

The relationship between "surface rights" and the right to mine is clarified by Mr. Gilmore's comment that, "The locator does not lose all of his surface rights if he does not file his verified claim. He does lose the vegetative resources, but such loss cannot interfere with the mining operations of the miner who, with his hydraulic workings or other open-pit mining, has the right to destroy the surface in its entirety. The act does not take away the rights of the miner to extract the mineral. The right to despoil the surface is secondary to the right to mine, as the act clearly states."

C. (refer to page 19 in text)

In commenting upon the problems that face a locator today in determining the sufficiency of his discovery, Mr. Gilmore states:

"I am well aware that the definition of "Discovery" as given to the general public by both the Forest Service and the Bureau of Land Management is as set forth in the 'prudent man' concept. However, in in actual practice and under the method of enforcement of that rule, both departments of government depart from it a considerable distance. Today in any hearing held to determine the question of the character of the land and to determine whether a valid discovery has been made on that claim, and in every case that I have had (and I have handled many) and in every other one that I have heard of or have seen the decision concerning it, the rule is that the discovery must be of sufficient value to prove that the mine may be operated at a profit, however small."

". . . If the location is for gold, the locator is faced with an almost impossible condition. For example a location when made in 1934 with gold at $35.00 per ounce, might easily have been a paying proposition in the earlier stages of development. In 1959 a far different condition faces the locator. The inflation of the dollar and greatly increased costs of mining make the 1934 ounce of gold worth about $16.00 in 1959 purchasing power. So the paying mine of 1934 would now be found nonmineral in character by the Bureau of Land Management, because it would not now pay to work."

And further,

"I have never seen an official definition of a 'prudent man' nor have I ever seen a prudent man rule applied except in the most arbitrary manner, simply because of the fact that it is incapable of being defined. No hearing examiner that I have seen and no judge on the bench in any court before whom I have practiced during the last 40-odd years, has ever been able to look into the mind of any man and determine whether that man is a prudent man or not. Finally, I never saw a prudent prospector nor did I ever see a prudent miner." ". . . Some of the best mines in the west, and particularly in California, that were producers before 1942, were operated, not by prudent men, but men who were at the time described as the greatest fools that ever adorned God's green footstool."

"Was it a prudent man who discovered the Argonaut Mine near Jackson? Would you call a prudent man one who would sink a hole a hundred feet in depth without a trace of mineral, in the face of all the expert advice in the country at that time that there was no mine there, and strike the apex of the Argonaut vein?"

D. (refer to page 67 in text) The Forest Service actually is not in a position legally to permit or deny bona fide prospecting on public lands within the national forests or as Mr. Gilmore writes:

"There is no difference whatsoever in locating a mining claim within those areas than outside."

And further, "The mere existence of a forest reserve is no deterrent to mining. It is true that a man who has a mining claim must obey the regulations relative to protection from fire, the cutting and removing of timber for sale and such things as that, but he has to obey the same sort of laws outside the forest reserve, where certain lands inside the forest reserve are withdrawn from all forms of mineral entry, and withdrawal is no different than similar withdrawls outside the forest reserve."

In the opinion of Mr. Gilmore,

". . . As proof of the limited authority of the Forest Service I quote herewith Section 1 of the Act of February 1, 1905, which is now 16 U.S.C.A. 472:

'The Secretary of the Department of Agriculture shall execute or cause to be executed all laws affecting public lands reserved under the provisions of section 471 of this title, or sections supplemental to and amendatory thereof, subject to the provisions for national forests established under subdivision (b) of section 471 of this title, after such lands have been so reserved, excepting such laws as affect the surveying, prospecting, locating, appropriating, entering, relinquishing, reconveying, certifying, or patenting of any of such lands.'

"Likewise, the Act of June 4, 1897, Section 1 thereof, now 16 U.S.C.A. 482, provides in the last sentence as follows:

'And any mineral lands in any national forest which have been or which may be shown to be such, and subject to entry under the existing mining laws of the United States and the rules and regulations applying thereto, shall continue to be subject to such location and entry, notwithstanding any provisions contained in sections 473-482 and 551 of this title.'"

INDEX

A

Abandoned excavations, regulations covering : 78
Abandoned claims, relocation of : 26
Abandonment, of tunnel site : 25, 29
Abstract of title : see under Title
Access to water, right of : 70
Adverse, against patent : 42
Adverse claims : 42, 63
Adverse possession, by cotenants : 47
    effect on assessment work : 37
Adverse relocation, claims open to : 36
    effect on resumption of labor : 41
    see also : Relocation
Advertising out a cotenant : 41
Affidavit, of annual labor : 35, 37
    see also under : Notice required
Agricultural ground, rights of locators on : 27
Alaska, filing adverse claims in : 63
Aliens, restrictions on : 12, 21
Amended location : 23, 33, 38
    essentials of : 26
Amended location notice : 48
    required for patent : 57
American Mining Law, by A. H. Ricketts : 3, 5, 7
American River, restriction of activities on portions of : 110
Annual expenditure, failure to contribute : 46
    suspension of : 37-38
    see also : Assessment work, labor
Annual labor : see Assessment work, Labor
Annual work : see Assessment work, Labor
Apex of vein : 29
Application for patent : 57, 60-62
Appropriation of water for mining : 69-70
Arizona, Cadastral Engineers office in : 64
    U.S. Bureau of Land Management office in : 64
Arkansas, filing application for patent in : 57
Asphaltic mineral lands, subject to State indemnity selection : 18
Assessment work : 34, 36-42, 55, 109
    distinguished from location work : 37
    excused by adverse possession : 36
    table summarizing suspensions of : 40-41
    tunnel development used as : 25
    see also : Labor, Resumption of labor
Association, proof of citizenship by an : 58
Association locators : 20, 23
Association placer claim : 21, 23
    annual expenditure required : 36
    discovery work on : 32
Atomic Energy Act : 17
    amendment to : 100-101
Atomic Energy Commission, definition of source materials by : 17
    information obtainable from : 65, 94
    uranium leases issued by : 14, 95
Attorney in fact : 57, 61
Averill, C. V. : 7

B

Bibliography : 89
Blind veins, not open to location : 20
Boundaries, claim void on discoveries without : 27
    established by patent : 42
    recording of : 34
    requirements for location : 22, 31, 33
Bradley, Walter W. : 3
Breach of trust, claim voided by : 27
Building stone, patenting claim for : 60
Bureau of Land Management : see U.S. Bureau of Land Management

C

Cadastral Engineer, District : 56
    Office : 56, 58, 59, 60, 63
Cadastral Engineers, list of offices of : 64
California, Cadastral Engineers office in : 64
    U.S. Bureau of Land Management offices in : 64

Lake beds, not open to location : 19
Lands not open to location : 18-19, 25
Lands open to location, defined : 12-13
    sources of information on : 13
Lead lode locations : 28, 31
Lead veins, in townsites : 25
Lease : 49
    definition : 44-45
Leasing Act minerals, protected by P.L. 585 : 95, 96, 97, 98, 99
    regulations for mining : 46
Leasing Acts, effects on assessment work : 36, 42
    locating on lands subject to : 16, 17
    provisions of : 13
    see also : Mineral Leasing Acts
Legal Guide for California Prospectors and Miners : 7
License, definition of : 44
License required, for buying ore : 83
    for obtaining retort sponge : 89
Lignite : see Coal
Litigation, effect on patent request : 58
Location, amendment of : 25
    California statutes governing : 30-35
    conflicting : 27, 42
    definition of : 20
    essentials of : 21, 29
    force and effect of recorded : 35
    lands not open to : 18-19, 25
    lands open to : 12-13
    subsequent : see Relocation
    U.S. statutes governing, 28-30
    void : 27
    voided by non-compliance with code : 32
    see also : Amended location, Lode claim, Mill-site location, Placer claim, Tunnel location
Location notice : see Notice of location
Location work, distinguished from assessment work : 37
Locator, definition of : 21
    rights of first : 27, 55
Lode claim, annual expenditure required : 36
    annual expenditure requirements suspended : 37-41
    assessment work on : 36-42
    discovery work required : 22, 32
    effect of townsite on : 26
    notice of location : 49-50
    patenting of : 56
    purchase price for patenting : 58
    recording of : 34
    see also : Lode location
Lode discovery, definition of : 19
Lode laws, restricted by Leasing Acts : 13
Lode location, allowable extent of : 28-29, 31
    definition of : 20
    essentials of : 21, 22, 23, 30-31
    see also : Lode claim
Lodes, claimed under placer patent : 61
Logan, C. A. : 7
Louisiana, filing application for patent in : 57
    leasing laws in : 55

M

MacDonald v. *Midland Min. Co.* : 33, 38
Manner of Locating and Holding Mineral Claims in California : 5
Map, showing township and range system in California : 110-111
    showing water pollution control regions in California : 73
Materials Disposal Act of 1947, amended by P.L. 167 : 14, 102-107
McGuire v. *Brown* : 69
McKinley Bros. v. *MacCauley* : 69
Merced River, restriction of activities on portions of : 110
Mexican grants, open to location : 12
Military personnel, suspension of assessment work for : 38
Military reservations, not open to location : 18
    open to location : 12
    State indemnity selection of mineral lands in lieu of : 18

to include survey notes and certificate: 33-34
to insure surface rights under P.L. 167: 15, 104
to mining claimants under P.L. 167: 104, 105, 106, 107
under "source materials" Act: 17
see also: Affidavit, Statement

O

Office Cadastral Engineer: 56, 58, 59, 60, 63
Oil, subject to leasing laws: 55
Oil and gas leases, locating on lands held under: 14
Oil fields, limitations of State indemnity selections in: 18
Oil lands, subject to State indemnity selection: 18
Oil shale, restrictions on locating: 13
    safety regulations on mining of: 46
    subject to leasing laws: 55
Oil shale lands, subject to State indemnity selection: 18
Open-pit mining, on stock-raising homesteads: 27
    surface rights in: 116
Option: 45, 52
Ore-buyers' licenses: 83-87
Oregon, Cadastral Engineers office in: 64
    U.S. Bureau of Land Management Office in: 64
Oregon Department of Geology and Mineral Resources, information available from:
    40

P

Parol, transfer of right of location by: 43
Partnership, mining: see Mining partnership
Patented land, not open to location: 19
Patented mining claims, protection of surface rights by: 15
    sources of information on: 13
Patents: 42
    application of assessment work toward: 37
    mineral: 55-65
        effect on water rights: 69
Penalties, for high-grading: 86-87
    for non-compliance with Public Resources Code: 33
    for violating Fish and Game Code: 76
Permit required, for hydraulic mining: 47-48
    for promotion of mining enterprises: 81
    to transport explosives: 78
    to use national forest land: 67-68
Petroleum, restrictions on locating: 13
Phosphate, safety regulations on mining of: 46
    subject to leasing laws: 55
Phosphate lands, subject to State indemnity selection: 18
Placer claim, annual expenditure required: 36, 37
    annual expenditure requirements suspended: 37-41
    assessment work on: 36-42
    locating on: 12
    discovery work required: 22, 32
    effect of townsite on: 26
    notice of location: 52
    patenting: 59-60
    perfecting: 33
    purchase price for patenting: 60, 62
    recording of: 34
    see also: Association placer claim, Placer location
Placer deposit, lode location void on: 27
Placer discovery, definition of: 20
Placer laws, restricted by Leasing Acts: 13
Placer location, definition of: 20
    essentials of: 21, 22, 24, 31
    under P.L. 359: 108
    see also: Placer claim
Placer mining, restrictions on power site reservations: 15-16, 108
    water pollution by: 73-75
Plat required, in applying for patent: 57, 58, 59, 60, 61
Pollution, definition of: 71
Pollution of water: 71-76
Posting on claim: 57, 58, 60, 61, 95
Posting lode location notice: see Notice of location, essentials of
Potash, restrictions on locating: 13
    safety regulations on mining of: 46
    subject to leasing laws: 55

64993   6-62   7,500   printed in CALIFORNIA STATE PRINTING OFFICE